Focusing on Laser Engraving and Decorating

Affordable, Versatile, and Creative Marking, Engraving, and Cutting

Michael L. Kleper

Boynton Beach, FL

About the cover: *The image shows the imaging head of the xTool M1, the first hybrid laser engraver and knife cutter.*

Focusing on Laser Engraving and Decorating

Affordable, Versatile, and Creative Marking, Engraving, and Cutting

International Standard Book Number: 9 780930 904074

Dedication

*For Gwen,
my love and inspiration*

Acknowledgments

During the course of my brief, deep-dive into the realm of laser engraving and cutting I have consulted many reference sources. Although too numerous to mention, I do list many of them in the Bibliography at the end of this book.

Many people were helpful in guiding me, or providing support for my research. Among them are:

Gil Araujo and Justin Tan at Ortur
Angela Cruise at Smokey Hill Designs
Jason Dorie at LightBurn
Jennifer Jae Gutierrez at Rochester Institute of Technology/IPI
Paul W. Harrison at LaserBond 100
Ryan Huddleston at Enduramark
Tom Jackson at Jackson Marking Products Company, Inc.
Oriya Klein at Crown Engraving
Brett Littlewood at King Gubby Designs
KaiLee Meisner at General Chemical Corp.
Prima Shi, Jasen Wang, Lily Tan at xTool
Mallory Sweet at Findlay3DPrinting
Dmitrii Voronov at Cartonus.com
Dave & Rebecca Zak at Art Resin

Warning & Disclaimer

Laser engravers/cutters are wonderous devices, providing for unlimited creative expression, potential commercial opportunities, and self-satisfaction and enjoyment. However, they do have the potential to cause physical and economic harm. When a laser head is active, the heat it produces will likely produce smoke, and under certain circumstances, flames. Fire is an ever-present danger that must be taken seriously. With proper precautions laser engraving and cutting can be a safe and satisfying hobby or business.

This book contains information gathered from users who have found success with various methods, formulations, processes and procedures that have worked well for them. Your experience may be similar…or not. While the author has used his best efforts to ensure that all of the information is accurate and complete, it is provided strictly for educational purposes. The reader takes full responsibility for any related actions that they may undertake.

The author cautions that the wide variety of materials and machines in use provides for the possibility of unintended consequences. Remember that most error is human error. It is best to keep a record of what works, and what does not. Readers have been provided with several recordkeeping pages in this book specifically for that purpose: Laser Engraving & Decorating Job Processing Records.

"Let the eye of vigilance never be closed."
Thomas Jefferson

Table of Contents

Preface

I know when my career trajectory began. As a young child in the 1950's I remember having had a printing set with very small pieces of rubber type (FIG. 1). At about age ten, while walking with my mom in downtown New Haven, Connecticut, I remember seeing a bigger version of my miniature press in a stationery store window. "That's what I want for my birthday," I told my mom. It turned out that the machine I saw was a mimeograph...not the sort of thing that a small boy could or should own.

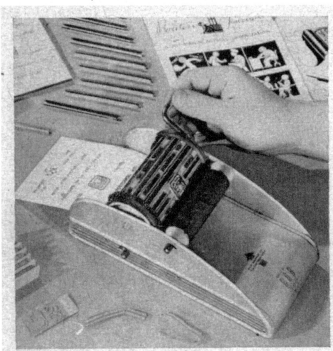

Toy Press Prints Type

Any child who can read can set type on this printing press. The rubber type snaps into slots on the press and is so grooved that it is impossible to set characters upside down. Made in three sizes by the Superior Marking Equipment Co. of Chicago, the press will also print pictures.

FIG. 1. This ad from Popular Science *magazine in 1951 showed a press similar to the one that launched my career in visual imaging.*

FIG. 2. An early cover from the Kelsey Printers' Supply Book.

Out of respect for my interest in printing, my dad found a company in nearby Meriden, Connecticut that sold hobby printing presses. The Kelsey Press Company sold an introductory package consisting of the Kelsey Junior Model R metal press with a 2" x 3" printing area, a composing stick, a type case with 6-point type, a tube of black ink, and some incidentals (FIG. 2). This printing press kit began what would become my life's work!

By the time I was in high school I had grown my hobby into a "printing business." I had a 5" x 8" Kelsey press, a motorized Golding Pearl platen press, and an A.B. Dick offset duplicator. I had built my own darkroom camera and darkroom, and could burn my own plates.

After high school I attended the world-famous School of Printing at the Rochester Institute of Technology in Rochester, NY where I earned three degrees. It was definitely the right place for me to be.

After graduation in 1969, I joined RIT's newest college, the National Technical Institute for the Deaf (NTID) as an Assistant Educational Specialist. I later wrote the proposal for an NTID Printing Program, and was one of its first faculty members.

By the time of my retirement in 2006 I held the Paul and Louise Miller Endowed Chair in the RIT School of Printing. Today I remain a Distinguished Professor Emeritus of the Rochester Institute of Technology.

So, what has this to do with laser engraving? Read on...

Michael Kleper, Summer 2022

1. Introduction

In the mid-1980's low-power lasers dramatically changed the way that we communicate; and how we store and distribute data. The word *laser* is an acronym for Light Amplification by Stimulated Emission of Radiation. Laser-imaged media first appeared in 1982 in the consumer market as the CD-ROM (compact disc read-only memory). With a storage capacity of 680 megabytes it quickly became a popular media format for the storage and distribution of computer programs, graphics libraries, music, videos, and databases (FIG. 1). Compact discs evolved in various forms so that eventually they could be written on by the end-user (Compact Disc Recordable (CD-R)), as well as be read. Over time, CD readers/writers became standard built-in components in personal computers.

FIG. 1. My book, The Illustrated Handbook of Desktop Publishing and Typesetting, *second edition, published in 1987, is believed to be one of the first popular titles to be released simultaneously in print and on CD-ROM. Ironically, the CD, which supposedly has a much longer shelf life than its paper version, can no longer be read due to a lack of compatible reader software.*

The lasers that were built into the CD writers had the capability to burn minute pits into the photo-sensitized surface on the back of a disc. Those pits, too small for the human eye to discern, could be optically read as the 1's and 0's that compose binary data, the language that a computer can process. In 1995 the CD format was superseded by the DVD (digital video disc, or digital versatile disc) with a higher capacity of more closely-spaced pits, and the capability to record on both sides. A dual-layer, double-sided DVD disc has a capacity of 17 gigabytes.

In 2004 the Hewlett-Packard Company introduced a new technology that not only recorded onto the back surface of an optical disc, but could burn a semi-permanent label onto its front surface (once the disc was manually turned over), without the need for ink or paper (FIG. 2). The technology was called *LightScribe,* and required a special disc reader/writer, special LightScribe media, and compatible LightScribe software.

FIG. 2. The front side of a LightScribe disc could be imaged using the LightScribe writer and software introduced by Hewlett-Packard. Attribution: Rico Shen, CC BY-SA 3.0 <http://creativecommons.org/licenses/by-sa/3.0/>, via Wikimedia Commons

The LightScribe disc surface incorporates a thin dye coating that the LightScribe laser uses to create a chemical change that produces a dark gray sepia color image. LightScribe discs with single monochromatic colors are also available. Although no longer in common use, die-hard users still use them, and blank discs are still available for sale on-line.

The next major leap in laser imaging came with more powerful lasers that can penetrate the surface of a substrate, producing an image, a perforation, a cut, or a combination of them. Known collectively as *Laser Engraving,* this process has swiftly evolved from a process reserved for manufacturers and fabricators, to one accessible to hobbyists, artists, and makers.

Laser engraving is a form of graphic imaging, producing permanent visible marks on a flat or curved surface. It is in many ways similar to the process of desktop publishing, which uses a low-power laser to form images on paper.

The derivation of the name *desktop publishing* is generally attributed to Paul Brainerd, president of the former Aldus Corporation of Seattle, Washington. Brainerd conceived the PageMaker program, which was the first credible software link between the Apple Macintosh and the Apple LaserWriter. At the time of its introduction in 1985, Page-Maker was the first program to easily integrate text and graphics on a page, thereby eliminating manual paste-up, and incorporating the composition process in a what-you-see-is-what-you-get (WYSIWYG) environment. PageMaker was acquired by Adobe Systems in 1994, and was replaced by Adobe InDesign in 2004.

Desktop publishing provides the user, usually the text originator or author, with the capability to produce reader-ready or camera-ready originals without the need (necessarily) for successive prepress operations. The tools of production are sufficiently compact to fit on a desktop and provide the user with total control over the content and form of the output (FIG. 3).

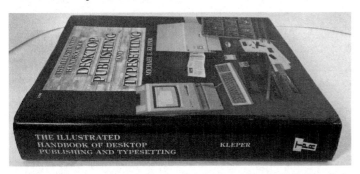

FIG. 3. *The first edition of* The Illustrated Handbook of Desktop Publishing and Typesetting *featured the main elements of the desktop publishing process on its cover. It was the first book to have one chapter output on the Apple LaserWriter, with the remainder output on a photo-typesetter. It is somewhat ironic that the book you are reading was created using very similar desktop publishing tools.*

The first credible desktop publishing system consisted of four major components: The Apple Macintosh, a highly customized Canon LBP-CX laser printer (sold as the Apple LaserWriter), the Adobe PostScript language, and a page-composition software package, the Aldus PageMaker program.

The Canon LBP-CX laser printer, used in the Apple LaserWriter, is the same engine that a number of other companies had chosen to use as the basis for their own laser printers (FIG. 4). It featured a 300 vertical dot pitch providing a measure of quality approaching (from a distance) that of professional typesetting, which ranges from 1200 to 2400 dots per inch. Despite its lower resolution, users accepted the quality level, much to the detriment of professional trade typesetters.

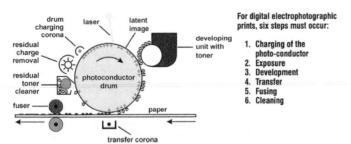

FIG. 4. *A diagram of the workings of a typical laser printer. Courtesy of the Rochester Institute of Technology Image Permanence Institute, Rochester, NY.*

In the heart of the Apple LaserWriter laser printer was the PostScript interpreter, which converted instructions from the Macintosh internal instruction set, called QuickDraw, into instructions that directed the operation of the laser. PostScript remained entirely transparent to the user, although it was possible to write instructions directly in PostScript by using communications software.

Representative components of desktop publishing are present in a contemporary low-cost, hobby-level laser engraving system. In this book we will look at various instances of the elements that form a viable laser engraving/cutting system.

First is the laser engraver itself. There are many low-cost laser engravers on the market, most of which fit into two major categories: laser diode and CO2. A laser diode system is composed of a semi-conductor component that produces lasing conditions at the diode's junction. It is the lowest-cost of the two. A CO2 laser generally has more cutting capability, more environmental safety considerations, and a higher price. Representative in this book are the Ortur Laser Master 2 Pro and the xTool D1 and M1 diode laser engravers. They were chosen based on their components, safety features, popularity, social media presence, third-party support, and price.

Software to drive the laser engraver is represented primarily by LightBurn. LightBurn is generally acknowledged to be the best solution for this purpose, although the field of options is presently small. There are versions of LightBurn for Macintosh, Windows and Linux computers.

The computer language that connects the images, type, and photos composed on the LightBurn screen is G-code. G-code is a standard programming language for the numerical control of automated machines. For the most part, G-code remains transparent to the user.

So, the laser printer (Apple LaserWriter) used in desktop publishing is represented by the Ortur and xTool laser engravers; the page layout software (Aldus PageMaker) used in desktop publishing is represented by LightBurn; and the page description language (PostScript) used in desktop publishing is represented by G-code.

We have moved from imaging on paper to imaging on almost anything!

We'll start our exploration of laser engraving/cutting with Air Assist, a necessary element in the process. We'll advance to the testing process, then recordkeeping, and go on to looking at popular laser engraver/cutter models. By the time you finish reading this book you should have a good overview of the entire workflow, and hopefully encouraged to give it a try yourself!

For those who want a quick overview of what a laser engraver is all about, skip to **Chapter 16, Summary: Laser Engraver Buyer's Guide.** And for those who want to see some of the many things that can be made with a laser engraver, see **Engrave and Cut Job Categories, page 119**, in the Appendices.

2. Air Assist

We start with air assist because it is not a standard feature in laser engraver/cutters...*but it should be!* The movement of air in a laser engraver/cutter is a critical factor to its safe and effective operation. An exhaust fan, as is well known, is a requirement to remove fumes and particles by pulling them from under the laser, and expelling them out of the work environment. Equally important is Air Assist.

Air assist is the addition of a precision nozzle, located near the laser head, that is connected to an air compressor, using a flexible plastic tube. The purpose of the air assist is to follow the path of the laser, moving fumes away from the area that the laser is imaging or cutting. Air assist works to:
- prevent the material from catching fire
- move noxious fumes away from the laser head to clear its path
- prevent the workpiece from suffering surface damage
- produce cleaner engraving or cut edges, reducing or eliminating additional clean-up operations
- reduce heat around the laser head, potentially extending its useful life
- potentially increasing the speed that the laser head can move
- reduce excessive heat from fumes that the laser re-heats
- reduce unsightly surface effects caused by smoke and other pollutants
- reduce surface discoloration and the generation of material residue
- help eliminate hazards to the operators' eyes and respiratory system
- increase the energy of the laser beam by eliminating smoke
- reduce residue that builds on the laser optics requiring cleaning or replacement
- reduce residue on a laser lens that can cause cracking, requiring replacement
- reduce edge scorches on the workpiece, which can require laborious sanding.

Professional air assist systems often use pure nitrogen or oxygen gas, creating an exothermic reaction that accelerates the effectiveness of the laser. Hobby-level systems use pressurized air.

The use of air assist not only helps to protect the health of the operator, it is a highly effective tool that protects the laser itself, and the materials that are processed (FIG. 1). By forcing a clean stream of air at the laser point, it can amplify the power of the laser by ensuring that more of the laser beam actually reaches the surface of the material.

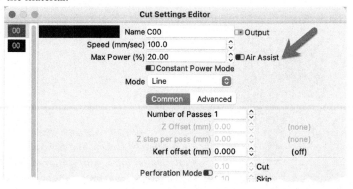

FIG. 1. Users of laser cutters that are produced with integrated air assist capability can turn the function on or off using a setting in LightBurn.

What air assist does in an automatic or semi-automatic way is exactly what an operator would do if an air assist was not available. Seeing smoke or fire arise from a workpiece, an operator would automatically respond by blowing, just as candles are extinguished on a birthday cake. Obviously, moving closer to noxious fumes or a flame is ill advised…thus an air assist is an essential addition to a laser engraver/cutter for health and safety reasons, as well as helping to ensure higher quality output, and extending the life of the laser.

Although air assist is important in reducing flames and surface degradation, it is not a fool-proof safety solution. At no time should a laser device ever be run without constant human oversight.

Air assist is absolutely essential for any laser cutting operation, and although it may be used for engraving, its use tends to intensify the output of the laser beam producing a slightly "dirtier" image. For some materials, such as wood, cardboard, and paper, the air assist may reduce the amount of char on the surface. The operator needs to exercise discretion in its use, since some materials may not benefit from it, or may actually suffer from its use (FIG. 2).

The focused heat of the laser, in the form of a very, very thin beam, incinerates the workpiece surface and produces what is known as a small "kerf." Kerf is the material that is removed during laser cutting. The controlled use of kerf in the design of a product may enable the material it is made of to bend or flex.

The Air Compressor
The air compressor is a pump that forces air through a tube to the nozzle. The air compressor must have sufficient air pressure (psi) and flow rate at the laser imaging/cutting site to remove the debris from the workpiece, which may be in the form of physical particles or smoke. The user must ensure that the inlet port on the pump is receiving clean air so that the laser work area is not compromised with airborne pollutants.

The Nozzle
The nozzle may be one of two types. A fixed nozzle may be attached directly over the laser lens. This type of nozzle is referred to as a "cone style," and it diverts the compressed air perpendicular to the cutting surface (FIG. 3). Its design serves to minimize surface residue and also provides the lens with protection from the immediate environment. The cone limits the space available between the lens and the material and can, in rare cases, touch the workpiece surface if it is uneven, or if a cut piece pops up.

An advantage of the cone style nozzle is the fact that it effectively seals off the lens surface from the pollution that is formed at the imaging surface.

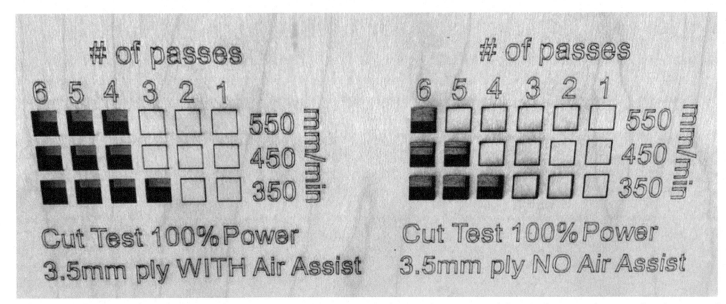

FIG. 2. *The example on the left clearly shows that air assist produces cleaner and more efficient cuts with less scorch. Notice, however, that the engraved areas are clearer with no air assist. Credit: Hannah Jakub Creations*

FIG. 3. *The air assist nozzle from Hannah Jakub Creations, available from Etsy.com, is made of brass and precisely fits a select number of diode laser cutters, including the Ortur Laser Master 2 Pro. Credit: Hannah Jakub Creations*

A detached nozzle, or "tube style," is typically flexible, and is attached by various means to the laser heat shield. Its flexibility provides for additional clearance when dealing with uneven material. Many nozzles of this type are produced using 3D printing, and can be positioned at an angle within 2-3 millimeters of the laser surface (FIG. 4). Many nozzles of this kind can be found on Etsy (https://www.etsy.com), and files for producing them can be found on Thingaverse (https://www.thingiverse.com).

FIG. 4. *The tube style air assist from King Gubby Designs is an inexpensive solution for adding air assist capability. It is available from Etsy.com either individually or as part of a bundle of Ortur accessories.*

The Tubing
The plastic tubing that connects the air compressor to the nozzle is a standard 3/16" clear flexible tubing.

3. Testing: Determining Laser Settings

There is a saying, based on what is called "The Law of the Instrument," attributed to Abraham Maslow in 1966, in which he said: "I suppose it is tempting, if the only tool you have is a hammer, to treat everything as if it were a nail." Now that you own a laser engraver you are doubtlessly consumed with thoughts of "what can I engrave next? Show me the nails!"

Certainly, the most frustrating part of using a laser is determining the correct settings for engraving and cutting. Over time, and with considerable experience, the user may be able to make an educated guess at settings intuitively; however, they are rarely consistently optimum. The only proper way to determine the right settings for your laser, for a given material, is to conduct tests and record the results.*

The process of determining the right settings for your particular laser engraver/cutter can be frustrating. One user described it this way:

"To be brutally blunt, laser engraving is a hell of a lot of luck, mixed in with a bit of knowledge and the availability of scrap, or soon to be scrap material, for testing. I've spent hundreds of hours and loads of money on something I am actually starting to think 'WHY'?

Although laser engraving is interesting, I have a feeling I'm rapidly running out of enthusiasm because of all the failures..."

History has taught us that process controls are key to any manufacturing operation. For example, years ago the printing industry used large cameras, called graphics arts or process cameras, to photograph pages (paste-ups) that would be printed (FIG. 1). They used large sheets of photo-sensitive silver-halide film, that were exposed using two basic parameters: the size of the lens opening (aperture) that let in light, and the length, in seconds, of the exposure to light. In order to determine the optimum exposure, a test target, or step wedge, was photographed along with the "copy." The test target consisted of a series of graduated tones, from white-to-black, that became visible after processing in a multi-step chemical bath. Reading the test target with an optical densitometer determined if the film negative was in the acceptable range. So too, the laser engraver produces images on the basis of two variables: speed and power. The graphic arts film had to run through a wet chemical processing system, which, over time, became weaker, and the control strips were an indicator. So too, over time, the strength of the laser can become weaker, and testing becomes the quality control indicator.

Tests consist of running the laser using a pre-designed, or self-made file, on a selected material. The results will apply only to the specific test material type. In order to minimize material waste the user should get in the habit of keeping off-cuts, and using the backs of poorly lasered projects.

The file is made of layers that combine machine variables, usually

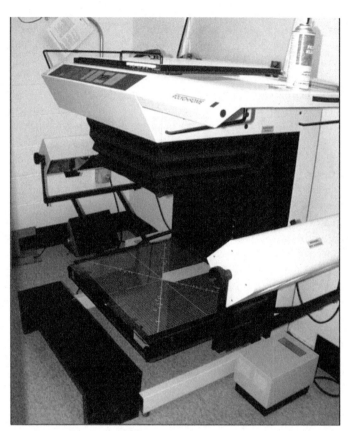

FIG. 1. A traditional graphic arts vertical camera has all of the components of a normal camera system (copyboard [target subject], lights, lens, and filmback), only larger. Producing consistent exposures then, is similar to producing acceptable laser engraver output today. They both depend on testing and the control of variables.

speed and power, to demonstrate the minimum time required to produce an acceptable output. The Speed is a function of how fast the laser head can move to the required X and Y coordinates. The Power is a function of the heat energy expended by the laser, in a range of 0 to 100%. The greater the power, the darker and deeper the engraving, and more likely that the laser can cut through a material. The test will show how fast the machine can move to produce an acceptable result.

One of the objectives of an engraving test file is to produce an output that shows a good gradation of shades from 5% to 100%. If there are no visible differences between the darkest adjacent shades, then the power is probably set too high. If there are no visible differences between the lightest adjacent shades, then the speed is probably set too high.

Making a Speed/Power Test Grid

Each material that will be engraved, or cut, requires a separate test to determine its optimum machine settings. As you will see, many

---

The exception is if the laser engraver manufacturer provides the settings right in the software, ensuring that engravings and cuts will always be executed correctly. This is the case for the xTool M1.

users have already done this for a variety of materials; and their test files, and recommended machine settings, can be sometimes be found in user group message boards, and other places on the Internet. The ultimate objective, long-term, is to amass a sufficient database of settings so that anyone can set-up their machine with readily available settings, and do so with confidence. As of this writing we are not there yet.

To manually prepare a test file we will use the layers feature in Light-Burn (see the chapter on LightBurn on page 46). Each element that will be engraved or cut always appears in the LightBurn workspace attached to a layer. The layer, identified by color, has default settings attached to it, namely a Speed of 100mm/sec, and a Power of 20%. The objective will be to produce a grid of small squares such that each square has its own separate speed/power value. Once we see this grid printed, we can decide which set of speed and power combinations best suits the needs for a given project.

We start by selecting an overall size for the test grid, usually based on a convenient small size that will be relatively quick to image, and does not waste valuable material. Let's select an arbitrary size of 5" square. We can assume that we have a pre-cut piece of material that size so that we do not have to wait for the laser to cut it, or produce unnecessary waste. We draw a square that size in LightBurn and as-

sign it to layer T1, which is tool notation layer that will not affect the laser, and is for reference only. It appears in the Cuts/Layers window with no assigned speed nor power (FIG. 2). It is assigned the type of "Frame" which will allow the laser engraver to properly position the target material on the machine bed for burning the test.

Next, in the upper left corner of the test pattern frame we make a small square, to represent the first element of the grid. We next apply a layer color of black, the first color in the color palette at the bottom of the screen. Note that the mode for all layers must be set to "Fill." This first box will become part of an array of boxes that represent various combinations of speed and power settings. To start the array, select the first box and open the Create Grid Array button. Set the number of horizontal columns to ten (FIG. 3), click OK. Next, select the first box on the left, open the Shape Properties window and set the Power Scale to 10 (FIG. 4). Repeat this action by selecting successive boxes and increasing the power scale by 10, so that the boxes represent the range of powers from 10 to 100. Next, select the first row, click the Create Grid Array button again, and create ten rows vertically (FIG. 5).

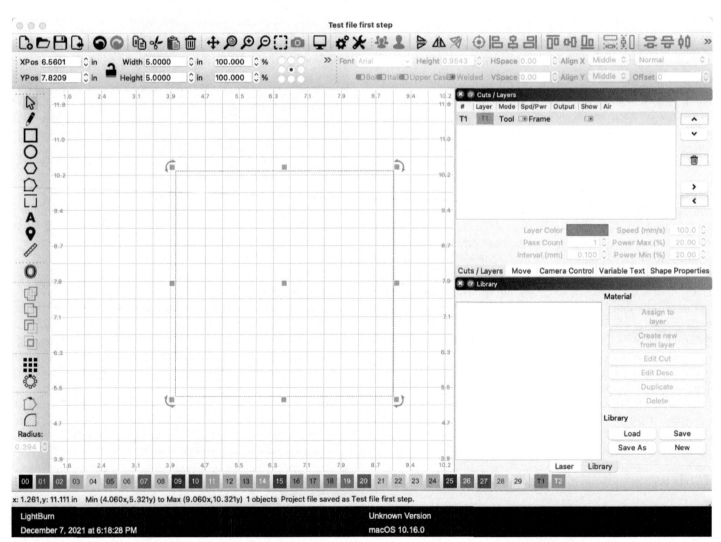

FIG. 2. The size of the test pattern, 5", is established in the workspace on a layer T1, which exists only as a visual reference.

The next step is dependent on how the targeted material will be processed, either engraved or cut, and what the characteristics of the workpiece material are. This will require some degree of judgement to determine what the workable range of speeds should be. Arbitrarily we can begin with a speed of 1000 mm/min. To do so, select the first row, which has already been specified as black, click on its Cuts/Layers setting, and enter the speed of 1000 and the power of 100. Continue selecting each row, assigning the successive color, and increasing the speed setting and decreasing the power setting until all ten rows have been set (FIG. 6).

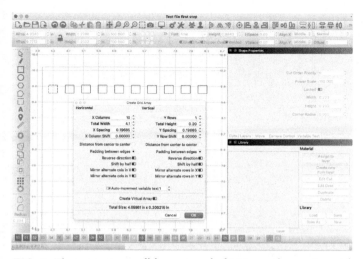

FIG. 3. The test pattern will be composed of 100 samples starting with one, and replicating them using the Create Grid Array button.

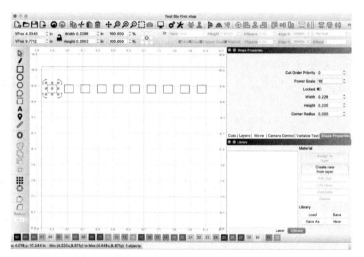

FIG. 4. Each box will have its own unique combination of speed and power.

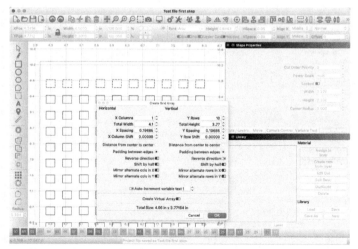

FIG. 5. The Create Grid Array function is used to quickly build the test pattern.

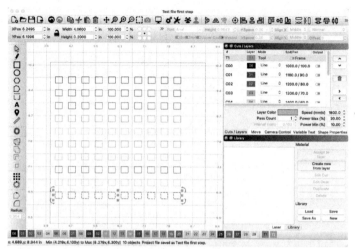

FIG. 6. The process of replicating rows makes the production of a test pattern fairly fast.

Next, label the horizontal axis with the power numbers using the Create Edit Text button. Resize the numbers so that they align with the boxes that they represent. Do the same for the speed numbers. Place a label at the top to identify the material being tested. Assign all text to the black layer so that it will print as dark as possible. <u>Most importantly, be sure all layers are set to Fill</u> (FIG. 7).

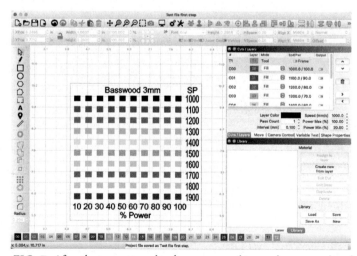

FIG. 7. After the test pattern has been composed it can be processed and evaluated immediately. The file can also be altered fairly easily to use for other materials. This process is based on the YouTube video by Phil Nolan entitled LightBurn Speed & Power Grid Tutorial (https://www.youtube.com/watch?v=9-NlhJAS6t4).

Test Grids

The objective of laser engraving and cutting is to set the parameters of the laser to the proper settings, in order to produce the sharpest, darkest engraving, or fastest, cleanest, cut. In some instances, the laser manufacturer provides the settings for a specific type of workpiece. In most others, the operator must determine the settings.

As mentioned, establishing the settings for a particular job is usually accomplished by producing a test grid, which is a series of small targets, each of which represents one instance of two variables, usually speed and power. There are numerous tests available, many free, many for sale. They can easily be found on-line, either in the file sections of Facebook groups, or in Etsy stores (FIG. 8).

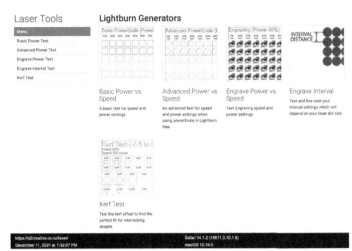

FIG. 9. *These LightBurn test file generators enable the user to produce test patterns that meet their specific needs.*

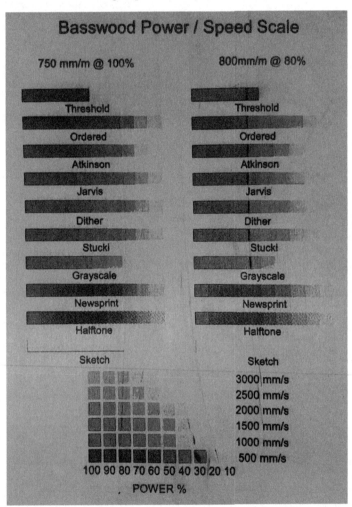

FIG. 8. *This test pattern, designed specifically for power/speed for dithered images created using Lightburn, is available as an instant digital download at the SemperCreations Etsy store for $2.*

Self-Generated Test Files

A very useful resource for generating LightBurn test files, with custom parameters, is available for free at https://o2creative.co.nz/laser/ (FIG. 9). The website has been created by Glenn Wilton of New Zealand, who has extensive experience in the design and print industry. Glenn's philosophy is that repetitive manual actions should be automated and customized to save time and effort (FIG. 10).

FIG. 10. *Here is a listing of the parameters that a user can set to create a customized test pattern for cutting.*

As of version 1.1.0 of LightBurn, the program itself can generate its own test grids. This function simplifies the process of determining the best settings for a new material. The test grid is generated by selecting Laser Tools>Material Test from the menu system and filling in the appropriate variables (FIG. 11). The user can preview the test grid prior to executing it (FIG. 12).

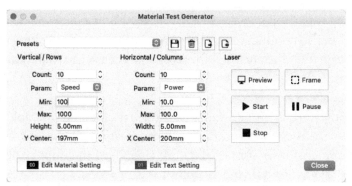

FIG. 11. *This Material Test Generator window enables the user to produce test grids easily and immediately.*

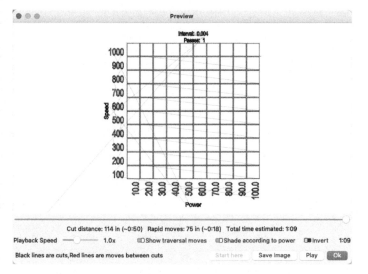

FIG. 12. *This preview provides verification of the test grid layout.*

Interpreting Test File Results: Embracing a Fotomat Mentality
Test grid files produce an array of possible settings. It is up to the user to select the one that they think is the best, and then transfer the settings to the laser engraver/cutter. In the case of a cut test, there is little margin for error, since a square is either cut through or not. In that case it makes sense to select the square that cut through with the least amount of power, or with the least amount of time. In the case of an engraved square or dithered pattern, one user may favor the color of a particular square while others may prefer a different square. It is a purely subjective judgement. It may be based on a personal preference for a lighter or darker color, on the preference of the buyer, on a whim, or some other factor.

Starting in the 1960's, first in Point Loma, CA, and later across the United States, a photo processing company came into prominence. Called Fotomat, its hut-shaped drive-up booths sprang up in mall parking lots, allowing for convenient and fast access (FIG. 13). The company's objective was to process and print photos overnight, at the lowest possible cost. It was able to do that by putting the time-con-

FIG. 13. *Fotomat drive-up kiosks were built for speedy transactions, in a minimum of space. Employees had to depend on near-by businesses for use of their restrooms. Photo courtesy of James Poolner.*

suming, and expensive process of quality control directly on the customer. Their policy was to reprint any photo that user did not like, letting the customer do the quality control. Fortunately for Fotomat, most customers liked almost all of their prints. Customers were less likely to be fussy about color balance so long as they could recognize who, or what, was in the picture. So too, with laser engraving: Despite how a test pattern may be interpreted, once a job is engraved, beauty is in the eye of the beholder.

4. Job Processing Recordkeeping

Certainly the most frustrating part of using a laser device is determining the correct settings for engraving and cutting. Over time, and with considerable experience, the user may be able to make an educated guess at settings intuitively, but, as stated previously, they are rarely optimum in all cases.

The key to effective and efficient laser engraving and decorating is to keep good records of successful machine settings for each specific material. It is usually the responsibility of the user to conduct tests to determine the optimum settings for each category of workpiece, and to log those results for future use. The enclosed forms enable the user to maintain accurate records for producing the best possible results...consistently.

These forms were designed to make recordkeeping easier...to efficiently maintain valuable information about laserable materials and their optimum machine settings. In addition, for those who produce goods for customers, the forms maintain important information for tracking project details and customer contact data. Having all of the important setting information available in a consolidated set of records provides a single touch-point for easy access.

The data stored in the forms can also form the basis for a workpiece inventory system, tracking material sources, cost of goods, pricing history, processing times, and other factors that determine the ultimate profit per job.

The data fields in the form also form the basis for the creation of a computer database that can track customers and maintain up-to-date business records.

These forms are available in book form at Amazon.com under the title, *Laser Engraving & Decorating Job Processing Record Book,* by Michael Kleper. https://tinyurl.com/498urjdk

Laser Engraving & Decorating Job Processing Record

Date:	Laser Model:		Operator:

Project Description:

Client/Customer:	Phone(s): ( ) ( )	e-Mail:

Special Instructions:

	Speed	Power	Passes	LPI	Est. Run Time
☐ Engrave					
☐ Score					
☐ Cut					

Photograph/Bitmap Parameters:

Workpiece Material(s):	Material Source(s):	Material Cost(s):

Material Characteristics (size, thickness, color, etc.):

Computer File Name/Location:

Pre-Treatment(s):

Post-Treatment(s):

Additional Tools/Processes:

Photo/Sketch:

Notes/Comments:

Selling Price:	Profit:	Delivery Instructions:

Laser Engraving & Decorating Job Processing Record

Date:	Laser Model:		Operator:

Project Description:

Client/Customer:	Phone(s): ( ) ( )	e-Mail:

Special Instructions:

	Speed	Power	Passes	LPI	Est. Run Time
☐ Engrave					
☐ Score					
☐ Cut					

Photograph/Bitmap Parameters:

Workpiece Material(s):	Material Source(s):	Material Cost(s):

Material Characteristics (size, thickness, color, etc.):

Computer File Name/Location:

Pre-Treatment(s):

Post-Treatment(s):

Additional Tools/Processes:

Photo/Sketch:	Notes/Comments:

Selling Price:	Profit:	Delivery Instructions:

Laser Engraving & Decorating Job Processing Record

Date:		Laser Model:			Operator:

Project Description:

Client/Customer:	Phone(s): ( )	( )	e-Mail:

Special Instructions:

	Speed	Power	Passes	LPI	Est. Run Time
☐ Engrave					
☐ Score					
☐ Cut					

Photograph/Bitmap Parameters:

Workpiece Material(s):	Material Source(s):	Material Cost(s):

Material Characteristics (size, thickness, color, etc.):

Computer File Name/Location:

Pre-Treatment(s):

Post-Treatment(s):

Additional Tools/Processes:

Photo/Sketch:	Notes/Comments:

Selling Price:	Profit:	Delivery Instructions:

Laser Engraving & Decorating Job Processing Record

| Date: | | Laser Model: | | | Operator: | |

Project Description:

| Client/Customer: | | Phone(s): ( ) | | ( ) | | e-Mail: |

Special Instructions:

	Speed	Power	Passes	LPI	Est. Run Time
☐ Engrave					
☐ Score					
☐ Cut					

Photograph/Bitmap Parameters:

| Workpiece Material(s): | Material Source(s): | Material Cost(s): |

Material Characteristics (size, thickness, color, etc.):

Computer File Name/Location:

Pre-Treatment(s):

Post-Treatment(s):

Additional Tools/Processes:

Photo/Sketch:

Notes/Comments:

| Selling Price: | Profit: | Delivery Instructions: |

Laser Engraving & Decorating Job Processing Record

Date:	Laser Model:	Operator:

Project Description:

Client/Customer:	Phone(s): ( ) ( )	e-Mail:

Special Instructions:

	Speed	Power	Passes	LPI	Est. Run Time
☐ Engrave					
☐ Score					
☐ Cut					

Photograph/Bitmap Parameters:

Workpiece Material(s):	Material Source(s):	Material Cost(s):

Material Characteristics (size, thickness, color, etc.):

Computer File Name/Location:

Pre-Treatment(s):

Post-Treatment(s):

Additional Tools/Processes:

Photo/Sketch:

Notes/Comments:

Selling Price:	Profit:	Delivery Instructions:

Laser Engraving & Decorating Job Processing Record

Date:		Laser Model:		Operator:

Project Description:

Client/Customer:	Phone(s): ( )	( )	e-Mail:

Special Instructions:

	Speed	Power	Passes	LPI	Est. Run Time
☐ Engrave					
☐ Score					
☐ Cut					

Photograph/Bitmap Parameters:

Workpiece Material(s):	Material Source(s):	Material Cost(s):

Material Characteristics (size, thickness, color, etc.):

Computer File Name/Location:

Pre-Treatment(s):

Post-Treatment(s):

Additional Tools/Processes:

Photo/Sketch:	Notes/Comments:

Selling Price:	Profit:	Delivery Instructions:

Laser Engraving & Decorating **Job Processing Record**

Date:	Laser Model:		Operator:

Project Description:

Client/Customer:	Phone(s): ( )	( )	e-Mail:

Special Instructions:

	Speed	Power	Passes	LPI	Est. Run Time
☐ Engrave					
☐ Score					
☐ Cut					

Photograph/Bitmap Parameters:

Workpiece Material(s):	Material Source(s):	Material Cost(s):

Material Characteristics (size, thickness, color, etc.):

Computer File Name/Location:

Pre-Treatment(s):

Post-Treatment(s):

Additional Tools/Processes:

Photo/Sketch:	Notes/Comments:

Selling Price:	Profit:	Delivery Instructions:

Laser Engraving & Decorating Job Processing Record

| Date: | | Laser Model: | | | Operator: | |

Project Description:

| Client/Customer: | | Phone(s): ( ) | ( ) | e-Mail: |

Special Instructions:

	Speed	Power	Passes	LPI	Est. Run Time
☐ Engrave					
☐ Score					
☐ Cut					

Photograph/Bitmap Parameters:

| Workpiece Material(s): | | Material Source(s): | Material Cost(s): |

Material Characteristics (size, thickness, color, etc.):

Computer File Name/Location:

Pre-Treatment(s):

Post-Treatment(s):

Additional Tools/Processes:

Photo/Sketch:

Notes/Comments:

| Selling Price: | Profit: | Delivery Instructions: |

5. The Ortur Laser Master 2 Pro

Low-cost diode lasers have been the impetus for the design of entry-level laser engraving machines. These machines have become very popular with hobbyists, product designers, prototypers, do-it-yourselfers, artists, makers, small business owners, and others. Such implementers have found success marking, engraving, perforating, and cutting designs, and engraving images on a wide variety of materials.

In its simplest form a laser engraver is composed of a highly focused laser beam, to concentrate light; controller electronics to move the laser with precision; a housing to enclose the components; and a surface on which to image. All of these elements working together can create quite remarkable output of both functional and artistic value.

The Ortur Laser Master 2 Pro (OLM2 Pro), introduced in June, 2021, has distinguished itself among low-cost laser engraving ma-

chines. The device has an accuracy of 0.08mm x 0.15mm, and a maximum speed of up to 10000mm/min., making it, according to the company, up to "three times faster than the average engraver in the market."* It has undergone extensive testing following more than nine months of research and development, all the while remaining responsive to user feedback and suggestions (FIG. 1).

FIG. 1. The Ortur Laser Master 2 Pro laser head maintains an agile stance, able to move quickly to any area within it's 400mm x 400mm workspace. Its relatively light weight makes it easy to be moved to work on items that cannot fit on its base.

*Ortur Laser Master 2 Pro: High Precision Laser Engraver For The Ultimate Engraving Experience, https://www.electronics-lab.com/ortur-laser-master-2-pro-high-precision-laser-engraver-for-the-ultimate-engraving-experience/.

The Laser
The power of a laser is measured in watts. The Ortur Laser Master 2 Pro is shipped with a 20W laser. Generally speaking, the higher the watt number, the more powerful the laser. Consumer lasers generally extend up to 120 watts, with those higher in laser power reserved for industrial manufacturing. The density of the workpiece material, such as wood, determines the laser power necessary to process it. A 20W laser has sufficient power to engrave a wide variety of materials,

but is limited in its capability to cut them. This deficiency can sometimes be overcome by passing the laser over the material a number of times, i.e. passes. The more passes, the deeper the laser penetrates the material.

The Ortur 445nm diode laser module has an input power of 20W and an optical output power of 5.5W, and traverses an imaging area of 400mm (15.7") x 400mm (15.7"). It has a pixel accuracy of 300 pixels per inch, a resolution about as fine as a desktop laser printer.

The disparity between the input power and output power of a diode laser, such as found in the Ortur, is due to the generation of excessive heat. The laser beam is formed by the conversion of electrical energy into light (photons) in the laser diode. Excessive heat translates directly into a loss of power. Buyers should be aware of the disparity between input and output power when shopping for a laser engraver. Some manufacturers advertise their devices by input power, some by output power. It is the output power that matters.

Laser movements perform one or more operations as they traverse a workpiece. They can impose a design, either typographic, line artwork, or photographic; or they can perforate, crease, or cut, in a precise pattern. In any case, the laser is controlled primarily by two functions: its speed, normally expressed in mm/m or mm/s; and its power, normally expressed as a percentage of maximum output. The power range is often listed as 0 to 1000, where 0 is 0%, and 1000 is 100%. Note that the Ortur Materials Reference uses this notation (FIG. 2).

Safety Features

Lasers are dangerous devices and must be treated with utmost care. Fortunately, the Ortur Laser Master 2 Pro has a number of safety features that help to prevent accidents and the potential for excessive smoke and, in the worst case, fire.

Built into the 32-bit motherboard is a G-sensor that detects any deviant machine movement or vibration, which will result in stopping the laser beam immediately. Likewise, should the USB cable disconnect, or the host computer system stop or sleep, the laser beam will turn off. If, for any reason the laser head stops unexpectedly, the beam will also turn itself off to prevent a fire. Should a fire ignite, the machine has a built-in flame detector that will stop the laser firing and movement. If an actual fire should ignite, it would be wise to have a fire extinguisher at hand, or a spray bottle of water. The water should be tried first since it will produce less of a clean-up problem and possible damage to the machine. As a precaution, the laser engraver should never be left unattended.

Another key safety feature is the prominent red Emergency Stop Button that sits within easy reach of the user, on the top of the controller enclosure in the front of the device. The laser will completely cease operation if the button is pressed. Pressing the button locks it in place. It must be turned to unlock and resume normal operation.

The laser engraver construction kit comes with a pair of protective green-tinted eyewear, although the user may want to investigate a more professional set of laser protection goggles, as well as having extra pairs for anyone working in the immediate area. The laser head

Materials Reference

Laser Master 2 Pro Materials Reference

(S=Strength, 1000=100%)

	LU2-4 Cutting	LU2-4 Engraving	Remark
1.6mm Plywood Plate	Cutting 300mm/min,S1000 Run 1 pass	Engraving 10000mm/min,S1000	Darker Colors, Better Results.
2.8mm Plywood Plate	Cutting 100mm/min,S1000	Engraving 10000mm/min,S1000	Darker Colors, Better Results.
4mm Plywood Plate	Cutting 100mm/min,S1000	Engraving 10000mm/min,S1000	Darker Colors, Better Results.
7mm Pine board	Cutting 100mm/min,S1000 Run 2 passes	Engraving 10000mm/min,S1000	Darker Colors, Better Results.
9mm Pine board	Cutting 100mm/min,S1000 Run 3 passes	Engraving 10000mm/min,S1000	Darker Colors, Better Results.
0.1mm Colored A4 Paper (Not White)	Cutting 4000mm/min,S1000 Run 2 passes	Engraving 9000mm/min,S350	The white paper is non-opaque, the result is not very good.
0.3mm Colored A4 Paper (Not White)	Cutting 1000mm/min,S1000	Engraving 9000mm/min,S700	The white paper is non-opaque, the result is not very good.
250g Kraft Paper	Cutting 1000mm/min,S1000	Engraving 9000mm/min,S500	Darker Colors, Better Results.
3mm Paperboard (Cardboard Box)	Cutting 300mm/min,S1000	Engraving 9000mm/min,S400	Darker Colors, Better Results.
0.7mm Leather	Cutting 600mm/min,S1000	Engraving 10000mm/min,S1000	Darker Colors, Better Results.
Non-woven fabrics (0.5mm, Dark Color)	Cutting 2300mm/min,S1000	N/A	Cannot cut the white one. It's transparent in fact.
Some Plastic Sheet (Dark Color)	Engraving 3000mm/min,S600	N/A	Some plastic sheets may be melt.
5mm Acrylic	Cutting 100mm/min,S1000 Run 3 passes	Engraving 10000mm/min,S1000	Need coat the dark color paper onto the transparent Acrylic plate.
Tin Wire	Melting	N/A	Cannot engrave.
Cobblestone	Engraving 100mm/min,S1000	N/A	Need coated with acrylic dye heat transfer film.
Ceramic	Engraving 100mm/min,S1000	N/A	Need coated with acrylic dye heat transfer film.
Powder Coated Metal Paint Sprayed Metal	Engraving 10000mm/min,S1000	N/A	Engraved in the layer of powder coating.
Plated Metal	Engraving 100mm/min,S1000	N/A	
Anodized Aluminium	Engraving 10000mm/min,S1000	N/A	It's the surface color turned to be other color.
Stainless Steel	Engraving 100mm/min,S1000	N/A	The Glossy finishing surface should be painted black by Marker Pen.
Copper	Engraving 100mm/min,S1000	N/A	

The results would be different in even same material with different finishing or different colors. So you need to adjust the speed and power rate based on different objects. Also, please adjust the focal length to be the best, make the focal spot to be the smallest. It couldn't engrave or cut directly: Glossy metal plate, Transparent materials, Reflecting materials, Some materials in white color or previous to light, etc. Then, you need to use the marker pen to black it to engrave.

FIG. 2. Ortur has lab-tested a variety of materials to provide suggested settings for both engraving and cutting. Due to wide material variations the user should use these settings only as a preliminary guide.

itself is fitted with an orange hood to offer a degree of built-in eye protection from the intense laser light. The hood can be moved up or down, or removed, although that would be inadvisable. The optional hood enclosure, which surrounds the entire device, provides the best protection for both the laser device and the user.

The process of heating materials, such as plastic and wood at high temperatures comes with the inherent potential for fumes, smoke, and other air-borne irritants. It's important to have proper and adequate ventilation to remove such pollutants from the environment. The exhaust fan built into the optional machine enclosure is made specifically for that purpose.

Some materials, such as leather, acrylic, and rubber, can produce toxic fumes that are dangerous, since they can cause immediate and long-term health problems. These materials, if they must be used, should be processed wearing a face mask, such as the KN95 or N95 used during the COVID-19 pandemic.

Anything in the immediate vicinity of the laser head has the potential to be impacted by its intense heat and light. It represents a possible hazard for physical harm if used improperly or without adequate precautions. Remember, safety first!

Assembly

The Ortur Laser Master 2 Pro is provided in a partially assembled kit that can be put together using a few tools, including a Philips screwdriver, and a minimum of technical knowhow. Users should set aside a good portion of a morning or afternoon for assembly, set-up, and testing. Well-illustrated instructions are provided in print, and in videos produced both by Ortur (https://www.youtube.com/watch?v=vhqyy1dn17E) and YouTube users (https://www.inov3d.net/ortur-laser-master-2-pro-laser-engraver/). All of the components are made of high-quality materials and fit together securely.

In essence, the device is constructed of a square frame composed of four extruded aluminum rails, two of which form the Y axis. The X axis, which is preassembled, fits into the two rails on the left and right of the frame. Ball-bearing plastic rollers ride on timing belts that are secured on the left and right tracks to control the precise stepper-motor movement of the Y axis. The X axis comes with its timing belt installed. The laser head, fastening hardware, wiring, switches, motherboard and other elements are positioned and secured to complete the assembly. Once assembled, the user should test for squareness by measuring from corner-to-corner.

Software

As has been mentioned earlier, software is the key to controlling the laser engraver, which does not come packaged with any software. Windows users have the option of using the free open-source Laser-GRBL software (https://lasergrbl.com), and Windows, Mac and Linux users can use the superior LightBurn software (http://lightburn.com) available for $60 per year. The LightBurn software is available with a 30-day unrestricted trial. In either case, the OLM2 Pro requires that the host computer be attached via a USB cable, unless the user has the optional Ortur Offline Control box, which enables the laser to be used independent of a computer. This is accomplished by outputting the composed job as a G-code file (see page 59), saving it on a TF card, and inserting the card in the offline control box.

Focus

In order for the laser to exert the maximum amount of its energy, for finer cut lines and more accurate engraving, it must be focused precisely on the surface of the target material for engraving, or at the base of the material for cutting. When focusing, the light from the laser is directed through a lens to concentrate its beam to a fine point. The OLM2 Pro has a fixed focus, meaning the distance from the bottom of the laser housing to the material should always be the same. This is easily measured using the provided metal cylinder that is stored in the front of the machine. This precision block has been factory engineered to provide accurate, repeatable focus. The laser head is adjusted up or down so that the cylinder slides precisely between the two focusing surfaces.

The metal cylinder provides a height of 55mm and is meant to provide the proper focus in virtually all circumstances. If, however the goal is to cut, then the lens should be focused directly on the machine bed.

The optional Ortur Z-axis lifting device is a module that provides additional height allowance for the laser (FIG. 3).

FIG. 3. The Ortur Laser Master 3 Pro Z-axis gives the user additional height allowance for focusing.

There may be instances where the user purposefully sets the laser out-of-focus a minute amount for the purpose of working with a wider line. Although not common, experienced users may find this technique useful in very specific circumstances.

The Base

During set-up and operation, the laser beam can sometimes extend beyond the target work material, or it may reposition itself outside the border of the material for any number of reasons. The laser may also misfire and mark areas around or beneath where it should be working. The operator may also inadvertently start the laser before the workpiece has been properly placed. For those reasons users always work on a base of some sort, so that stray laser marks do not damage a tabletop or other pristine work surface.

A base can be made of almost any material, provided that it is sufficiently hard and flat. Plywood or MDF is commonly used since it is relatively inexpensive and plentiful, and can be adhered fairly easily under the OLM2 Pro so that it remains stationary. A base of this type is usually referred to as a *sacrificial* or *spoil board,* since its only purpose is to protect what lies beneath it, and over time will need to be replaced. The actual laser frame legs can be attached to the base for stability using third-party leg restraints as shown here in FIG. 4.

FIG. 4. These inexpensive leg restraints are held in position by two screws and ensure that the laser device does not move or vibrate. Credit: MakerBoss3D, available on Etsy. https://www.etsy.com/listing/968799413/ortur-laser-master-2-leg-retainers?ref=shop_home_active_3&crt=1

It is common for a user to engrave a grid directly on the base. This provides a handy visual guide for aligning one or more pieces to be processed.

If material is to be cut, and the laser beam is focused directly on the base, the user should consider a surface that has a pattern of holes, like a honeycomb. This allows the laser to extend its beam beyond the back of the target material instead of directly onto what is probably a flammable wood surface. The cut-out pattern base material, usually made of metal, allows for air through the back of the work piece, and reduces the chance for char, smoke, or fire.

While the laser is operational there are forces at work on the base that can cause the target material to move. It may be from the movement of air from the exhaust, air from the air assist, air from the movement of the laser head itself, incidental vibrations, or occasional movement of cables or hoses attached to the frame. Any of these things can com-

promise the precision of the lasering operation. For this reason, the user should devise some way to keep the target work area flat and in place, holding it down with something like clips, stops, magnets, tape, vacuum, or a custom jig.

There may be instances where a base is not needed, such as if the laser engraver must be moved to the place where the engravable object is located. A big item, such as a door or bench, large sign, or other large-format item can itself be the base onto which the laser engraver is placed. Alternately, the laser engraver may remain in a fixed position and the item is moved, in register, beneath it, in precise increments. In either case, physically moving the entire laser to another location, and using it in a nonpermanent set-up, can add to, and complicate, safety issues.

In May, 2022 Ortur introduced an Extension Kit that increases the Y axis travel distance to 800mm, thereby doubling its engraving area (FIG. 5). The kit includes reinforced aluminum alloy rails, brackets, cabling, belts, and hardware, thereby making the confined work area 400mm x 800mm.

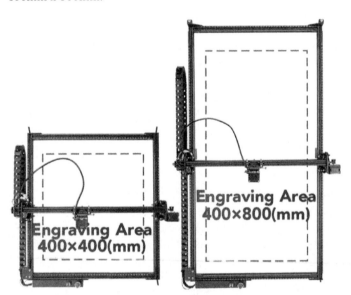

FIG. 5. The DYI Extension Kit, installed in as little as ten minutes, can double the work area of the Ortur Laser Master 2 Pro. Other kits are available for other Ortur models. Courtesy: Ortur.

Height Adjustment
Most workpieces easily fit between the surface of the base and the laser, with that distance being adjusted for proper focusing by moving the Z-axis up or down. When more space is needed to accommodate the height or thickness of a workpiece then the entire Ortur assembly frame must be raised. This is accomplished by inserting objects of some sort under each frame leg. Since Ortur does not provide the means for lifting the frame, users have resorted to innovative ways to meet the need. Among them are:

Duplo® and compatible Blocks: These plastic interlocking blocks (2 x 4 blocks, 2.5" x 1.25") are the large-scale version of Legos®. They are a convenient size, and of suitable strength, to elevate the Ortur frame several inches off of the work surface. The notch in the custom 3-D-printed accessory provides more than adequate support. See FIG. 6.

STACKABLE "BRICK" FEET

Blocks not included.

FIG. 6. The stackable brick feet accessory kit consists of two parts: a bottom section that is attached to the work base, and a top section into which the Ortur legs fit. The user supplies the Duplo blocks that fit in between the two. Photo courtesy of King Gubby Designs, https://www.etsy.com/listing/960698820/ortur-laser-master-2-retainer-feet?ref=shop_home_feat_4&bes=1.

Bed Height Adjusters: These risers consist of two plastic pieces that can be used alone, or in combination, to raise the Ortur frame 3, 5, or 8 inches. The risers are exceptionally strong since they are designed to support a heavy bed with one or more adults (FIG. 7).

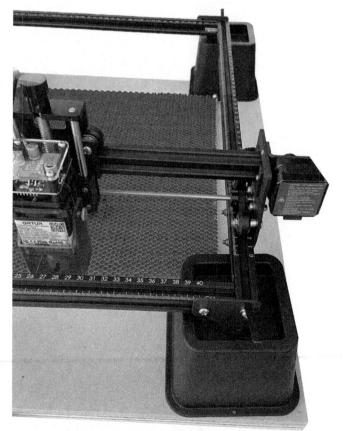

FIG. 7. Bed height adjusters, always sold in sets of four, offer a way to easily raise the height of the laser engraver in graduated steps.

Canned Goods: In a pinch a number of ordinary household items can be used to raise the Ortur frame. Soup cans, for example, are sufficiently strong to serve the purpose, although they should not be stacked, out of a concern for stability.

Belt Tension

During assembly the drive belts are adjusted so that they are snuggly secured to eliminate any "play" that can distort the movement of the laser. Over time the belts can loosen or wear, and the degradation will manifest itself in any number of ways, such as misaligned raster lines and other anomalies. The belts can be tightened manually by loosening the set screw, pulling on the belt, and re-securing it. Users can also install third-party belt tensioners that can simplify the process of maintaining proper belt settings (FIG. 8).

FIG. 8. This set of belt tensioners simplifies the process of locking in additional belt tightness. Photo courtesy of King Gubby Designs.

Contact

Ortur, or more accurately, Dongguan Ortur Intelligent Technologies Co., Ltd.,* is a worldwide high-quality manufacturer and distributor of 3D printers and laser engravers. The company introduced their first laser engraver in 2019. As a customer-focused company, their objective is to design their products to deliver the best user experience possible.

The company, considered in the top three in their field worldwide, was founded in March, 2018 by a small group of young engineers intent on tapping into the potential of the growing maker market, first addressing the area of 3D printing. They have expanded into laser engraving and plan future products in CNC machining. Their motto is "Imagine It, Design It, Make It!"

*Company mailbox: ortur@ortur3d.com; Official website: www.ortur3d.com

6. The xTool D1 10W Laser Engraver/Cutter

The xTool D1 10W (FIG. 1) has been engineered by industrial designers who have produced high-end CO2 laser engraver/cutters, and who have applied their design and manufacturing know-how to enter the diode laser market. The xTool D1 is the result of their mission to enter the hobbyist market with a machine that excels in significant ways, including a motion accuracy precision of up to 0.01mm.

The parent company of xTool is Makeblock, a world-renowned company in the STEAM education space, founded in 2013. It is a leading provider of technologies for education, with more than 100 worldwide distributor partners. xTool was launched in 2019 with its first product, the xTool Laserbox CO2 laser engraver/cutter.

FIG. 1. The xTool D1, available as either a 5W or 10W version, is the company's first entry in the diode laser market. Credit: xTool

Construction

The D1's solid aluminum alloy construction is noteworthy since the xTool opted for the strongest materials, yielding a laser head that glides smoothly on stainless steel wheels along a wear-resistant guide rail structure, producing very impressive laser spot accuracy and consistency, with a minimum of vibration. The X and Y axis movement is controlled with two stepper motors, contained within the frame, advancing the pre-installed belts that deliver the laser head to its required coordinates. With the stepper motors, belts, and electronics concealed and protected within the frame, the overall look of the D1 is exceptionally clean, sleek, and high-tech.

Assembly

The assembly process can take as little as 15 minutes for an experienced assembler, or 30 to 45 minutes for a beginner. The fit-and-finish of the parts is exceptional. Several of the components, such as the belts, stepper motors, and motherboard have been pre-assembled, not only reducing assembly time, but ensuring that precision parts have been factory set.

Focus

Since focus is a critical element in producing usable output, the D1 is notable since it offers a best-in-class solution. A finger screw on the left side of the laser head loosens it so that it can be moved up and down, closer or further from the workpiece, along the Z-axis. The amount of upward movement is significant, since it determines how high or thick the material that can be processed. A focus device, called the *ranging rod* (FIG. 2), is built into the right side of the laser head and is held in place

FIG. 2. The ranging rod, shown here in mid-position, offers the easiest solution to setting accurate focus quickly and consistently.

magnetically. The user flips the rod down, adjusting the laser head until the rod touches the workpiece. The laser is now in focus, the set screw is tightened, and rod is returned to its upright position. The built-in rod is not only convenient, but it is always immediately accessible.

The maximum speed of the laser head is 10000mm/min. which is considered exceptionally high.

The rated electric power of the laser head is 40W, outputting a laser power of 10W. Rather than sell the device as a 40W laser, xTool only touts its true laser strength of 10W. This honest assessment of the true laser rating is, unfortunately, a rarity in the industry.

The laser head is a bit of an engineering marvel, given that it contains two 5W laser emitters; one directed straight down, and a second directed at a 45 degree mirror (FIG. 3). They are cooled

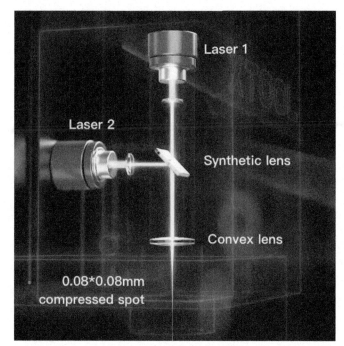

FIG. 3. xTool rates the power of the two 5W laser beams combined to be equivalent to a single 15W laser cutter. Credit: xTool

FIG. 4. The purchase of the xTool Rotary attachment includes this set of extension legs that easily screw into the device's built-in legs to raise the unit.

by a built-in fan, that despite its strength, is relatively quiet. The dual lasers produce a very small, square laser spot of 0.08mm x 0.08mm which produces high-resolution images, and clean, smooth cuts. The square dot shape is superior to other lasers, such as the Ortur Laser Master 2 Pro, which is rectangular.

The work area of the D1 is about 17" x 16" which is more than sufficient for accommodating most of the projects that would be appropriate for such a device. Despite its size it weighs only about 5kg (about 11 pounds), meaning that it can be moved and repositioned easily by one person.

The D1 is provided with legs that raise it off of the worksurface to accommodate a range of workpiece thicknesses. The space on all four sides of the frame allows the user to slide materials into the active work area. Additional-cost legs can be purchased to extend that height to allow for the additional space as required for a rotary device. These optional legs screw easily into the attached base legs and match their size and color (FIG. 4).

Another unique element of the laser head is a built-in red crosshair light that indicates where the laser will fire. This indicator is safe to view without safety goggles, and despite the fact that it is offset from the actual laser lens, the software accounts for this discrepancy and properly positions the laser when firing. Users should not underestimate the importance of accurately aligning the laser head in relation to the workpiece.

Safety

The D1 was designed to provide an effective, efficient work experience with safety considerations built-in. The bottom of the laser head, closest to the workpiece, is surrounded with a light shield. The shield, a custom-fit piece of orange acrylic, allows the user to easily see that the laser is functioning, and protect

others in the vicinity who may not be wearing safety goggles. Of course, proper eye protection should be worn by everyone within the work environment. The operation of the laser will stop automatically when the machine senses movement or a tilt, as well as when USB or WiFi communication is interrupted.

During operation, the heat of the laser, reacting to the surface of the workpiece, will produce, to varying degrees, noxious smoke, soot, and other odors. Adequate ventilation, with the use of an enclosure and exhaust fan, repositioning the laser device near a window, or using fans to direct the airborne contaminants out of the environment, should solve this issue.

Workflows

The xTool D1 is unique in that the user is provided with three connection options: The standard USB cable connection, WiFi, and offline, with the use of the provided TF card. The TF card can contain only one job at a time. When a new job is sent, it overwrites the current job. A job on a TF card is processed by pressing the device button on the right front of the machine frame. These options mean the connection is not limited to the length of an available USB cable.

The D1 has one of the most direct and simple workflows, assuming that the connection has already been made:

1. Position the workpiece
2. Adjust the focus.
3. In the software...
   a. Select the connection mode
   b. Select Engrave, Cut or both

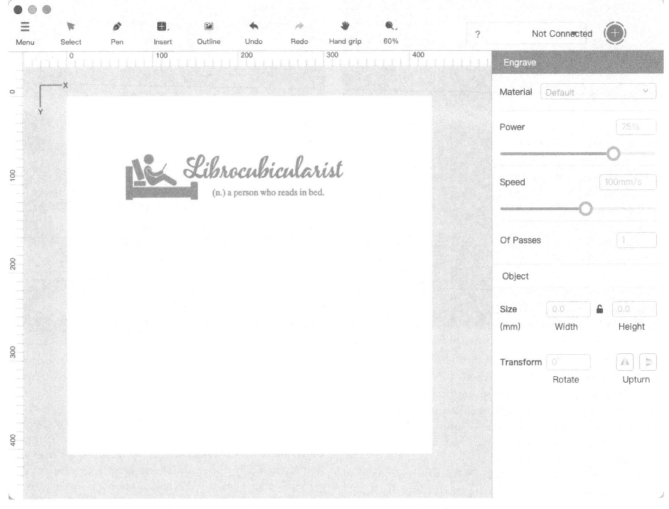

FIG. 5. The Laserbox Basic work area is uncluttered, with only the core capabilities available.

c.   Select the workpiece type
d.   Position the laser head relative to the work-piece
e.   Press Start

Software

Bundled with the D1 is proprietary software called Laserbox Basic (FIG. 5), which is a version of the software used with the CO2 laser engraver marketed by xTool. The software, which uses G-code to set the position of the laser head, has rudimentary capabilities that will help the user, particularly those new to the technology, get up-and-running quickly. It incorporates the machine settings that are needed to get good results from a wide variety of materials, such as various woods and acrylics, without the need for running time-consuming tests (FIG. 6).

The program incorporates its own options for Undo, Redo, Cut, Copy, Paste, Delete, and Select All, in the Edit Option in the main menu, rather than use the commands from the Operating System directly; although the key commands do work (FIG. 7). The program provides primitive shapes, including line, rectangle, rounded, oval, star, heart, and text. The Outline option (FIG. 8) creates a simplified line art tracing from a shape, saving

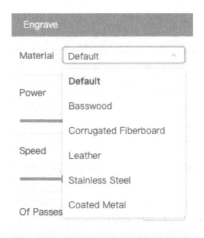

FIG. 6. The user has only to select the workpiece material and the program will set the necessary power and speed.

the laser the time and energy necessary to fill it in.

Before a job is sent to the laser the user must ensure that the laser head is properly placed, so that the job will be burned in the exact position necessary. The first step is for the user to position

FIG. 7. *The Laserbox Basic menu provides only the most rudimentary commands.*

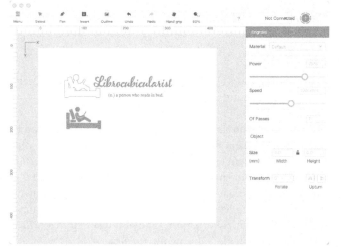

FIG. 8. *The Outline option creates an outline of a shape to reduce processing time.*

the laser using the red cross-hairs, and then hit the Frame button to see where the image will appear. Based on the outline revealed by the cross-hairs, the user can either adjust the position of the laser head or the workpiece.

FIG. 9. *The user can define the incremental movement of the laser head as it frames its intended image*

The travel of the laser head during this framing step is controlled using the Laserbox Control Panel (FIG. 9). The user can set the speed that the cross-hair will advance, and how much it will advance with each step, as executed using the compass arrows.

The iPhone/Android app is very simplistic, offering only two options (FIG. 10). The user can engrave an image that they have captured on their phone, or engrave one that is among the small number in the contained gallery (FIG. 11).

FIG. 10. *The two default options for the xTool D1 iPhone app are Quick Engrave and Gallery.*

FIG. 11. *The built-in gallery contains vector images in categories that include animals, food, flora, and others.*

Fortunately, xTool D1 is compatible with LightBurn, unlocking its full capabilities. LightBurn is considered the software standard for controlling laser engravers and cutters.

Laser Positioning

Unlike the Ortur Laser Master 2 Pro, which uses absolute positioning, the D1 uses relative positioning. What this means is that the Ortur uses built-in limit switches to ensure that the laser head always starts from, and returns to, the 0,0 starting coordinates, or Home. In LightBurn, for example, when the user places their design at a certain set of coordinates, the Ortur knows how to position itself at precisely that location. The D1 uses relative positioning, meaning that the user positions the laser head using the lighted red cross-hair, and indicates in the software, where on the design the laser should begin working.

The always-on red cross-hairs are a significant benefit, since the user can position a workpiece anywhere in the laser bed, and manually move the laser head to the desired start position.

Workbed. The proprietary Honeycomb Working Panel set is an optional accessory made from aluminum and iron (FIG. 12). It fits on the working space of the D1, protecting the surface on which the D1 sits, and diverting the exhaustion of smoke

FIG. 12. *The xTool Honeycomb Working Panel consists of two pieces: the honeycomb top panel, with imprinted mm increments along the left and bottom sides, and a rigid aluminum base. Credit: xTool*

through its channels. The surface is magnetic, making it possible to secure workpieces in place, either directly, if they are thin, like paper or cardstock, or indirectly, for thicker workpieces, in custom user-made magnetic jigs.

Air Assist. An air assist attachment adds a proven and trusted method for removing smoke and other harmful airborne particulates from around the tip of the laser (FIG. 13). In addition to keeping the laser lens cleaner, it is also the primary means by which smoke, char and burn marks are reduced or eliminated from the surface of workpieces when laser cutting. Particularly noteworthy is that the use of air assist can reduce the number of passes required for cutting, thereby reducing processing time. The xTool D1 air assist, designed as an integrated unit for the D1, is distinguished by its small, quiet, pump, its low level of vibration, and its significant amount of air movement.

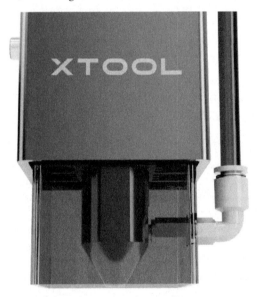

FIG. 13. *An air assist unit, such as the one designed for the xTool D1, is an essential add-on, producing higher quality output in less time. Credit: xTool*

Rotary Attachment
xTool Rotary. The D1 rotary attachment (FIG. 14), unlike the Ortur Rotary, comes completely assembled. It is engineered to work seamlessly with the Laserbox Basic, engaged by simply selecting the "toggle for cylindrical" option in Laserbox Basic. To connect the device to the D1 the user simply plugs its cable into the control board, and it is ready to use.

The rotary enables synchronized engraving on cylindrical objects, such as water bottles, drinking glasses, and mugs. It slowly turns the object as the laser head traverses, burning the design onto its surface.

xTool RA2 Pro. xTool RA2 Pro (FIG. 15) distinguishes itself not only as the first second-generation rotary, but also as the first to operate in four distinct modes, greatly expanding the realm of objects that can be precisely, and securely, held in position for engraving. It is shipped pre-assembled and supports both

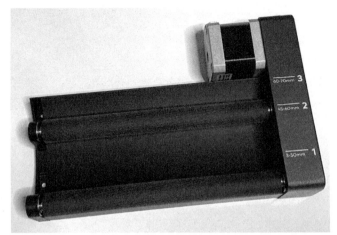

FIG. 14. *The xTool Rotary attachment enables the engraving of cylindrical objects.*

the xTool D1 and M1 as well as compatibility with AtomStack, Ortur, Twotrees, and NEJE.

The engineers who designed the RA2 Pro did in-depth research into the entire realm of cylindrical and round objects that could benefit from the engraving process. They designed a device with adjustable attachments that can easily adapt to a wide range of item shapes. Their work examined the shortcomings of the first-generation roller rotaries with the objective of accommodating a wider variety of objects, and also insuring that articles remain securely in place during processing.

The RA2 is essentially a chuck, a versatile radial clamp that holds a rotating object in place as it rotates under the laser head. While the chuck is dressed with the suitable set of jaws to hold the top of the object tightly, the bottom of the object is held level using the tail leveler height adjuster, which supports the bottom of the object on two height-adjustable ball-bearing rollers. This configuration simplifies the engraving of objects that have different or varying diameters from top to bottom. In addition, the device supports mugs with handles, and enables the chuck to be turned 180 degrees so that it is no longer restricted by its base.

The RA2 has its own stepper motor, which plugs into the laser engraver motherboard.

FIG. 15. *The xTool RA2 Pro greatly expands the variety of cylindrical and spherical objects that can be engraved. Credit: xTool*

The device works with xTool software as well as LightBurn. Set-up requires measuring the circumference of the object using the supplied ribbon tape measure. A bubble level, also provided, is used to confirm that the object is parallel with the laser head, confirming that it will remain in focus during engraving.

In order to accommodate jaws that support even more objects, xTool provides free 3D print files so that users can produce their own sets of jaws, up to 112mm.

There are four distinct ways to use the RA2:

1. In a manner similar to the original rotary, the rollers are arranged to accommodate the object, with the leveler accessory positioned at the bottom, adjusted to bring the object in a perpendicular position to the laser using the screw drive dial.
2. The rollers are removed and the chuck is attached. Attachments connected to the chuck allow a number of options for holding a diverse collection of cylindrical objects.
3. With the chuck attached, a round object can be secured in the chuck jaws, held in place with the suction cup holder attachment.
4. The set of three metal stems can be screwed into the chuck to secure rings, bracelets, and similarly shaped objects. This configuration can be used to engrave on the outside of a ring, with the metal stems holding it with inside tension. If the RA2 is lifted on an appropriate angle, so that the inside of the ring is exposed to the laser, and the stems hold the ring from the outside, then an inscription can be engraved inside the ring.

These various scenarios ensure that the widest variety of cylindrically- and spherically-shaped objects can be professionally engraved.

xTool Enclosure

The xTool Enclosure, introduced in June, 2022, is a creative solution for protecting an open-frame laser engraver, such as the xTool D1 (FIG. 16). The design of the enclosure makes it suitably generic to fit a variety of similarly-sized laser engravers sold by competitors.

Unlike other enclosure solutions, made from metal, wood, or plexiglass, the xTool Enclosure is light-weight (7.49 lbs). The sides are constructed from four layers of material, the inner-most of which is composed of flame-retardant polyester fabric 600D. The lower material costs account for a substantially less expensive enclosure.

The components, which are foldable, are easily stored; and in their flattened state are easily moved. The sides of the enclosure are assembled using hook and loop fasteners, making it quick to assemble and to break down. The outside surfaces, made of imitation leather (polyurethane), are very easy to clean. The side on the left includes a Velcro elastic strap that can hold a variety of tools, while the side on the right has a series of cut-outs for

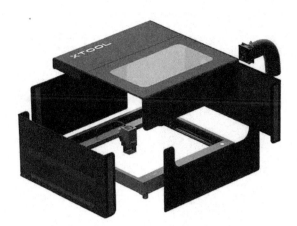

FIG. 16. The xTool Enclosure is an inexpensive way to shield the user from air-borne particles given off by the laser.

ventilation and cabling. The cabling cut-outs conform to the D1 power and USB ports, and properly align if the enclosure needs to be raised to accommodate a rotary attachment or a thick workpiece.

The enclosure has been designed for adequate ventilation, with fresh air entering through the air inlet on the left, and exiting through the exhaust fan (included) on the right. Exhausted air is cleared through a 2.0m flexible pipe composed of double-layer nylon cloth, that removes up to 99% of airborne contaminants. The assembly can also dampen any noise generated by the laser engraver components.

The user maintains access to the work area through a top lid that is held open with limit ropes on the left and right. The lid has a viewing window composed of yellow polycarbonate that filters out the harmful blue light of the laser while allowing a full view of laser processing.

The xTool 20W Diode Laser Module

The xTool 20W Diode Laser Module was rated as "the most powerful diode laser module in the world," at its release in late June, 2022. It is capable of cutting 10mm hardwood or 8mm dark acrylic in a single pass.

The significance of the laser module, which can be retrofitted on the xTool D1 laser engraver/cutter, is that productivity can be increased 200-250%. Users can produce more, faster; and work with harder, stronger, thicker materials, allowing for a significantly broader variety of marketable products.

The laser beam is formed by concentrating four 5W beams through a reflector, converging them into a single beam that exits a convex lens. The laser beam provides a laser head engraving speed of 10000mm/min., with a spot size of only 0.08 x 0.15mm.

The laser, which was released at a price of $599, represents a significant investment, approximating about half of the cost of the

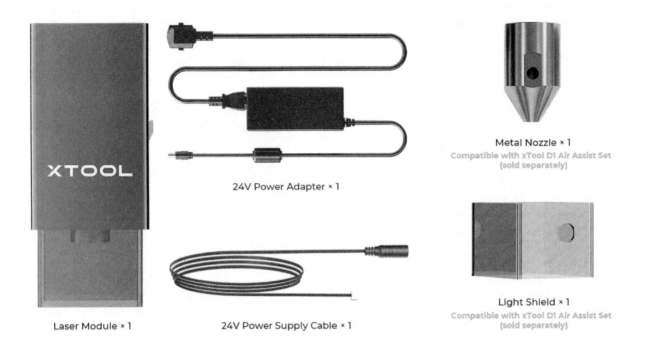

FIG. 17. The xTool 20W laser module includes all of the parts necessary to upgrade the xTool D1.

xTool D1 itself. Its cost can be justified by the significant time it can save, and the resulting competitive advantage it provides.

Maintenance
The laser head has an expected life expectancy of 8000-10,000 hours, and will, as is the nature of lasers, degrade over time. One of the things that will shorten its life is running the power at 100% for extended periods. This should be avoided. Rather than running at 100% the user can decrease the speed, or increase the number of passes.

Routine maintenance is fairly easy. The light shield must be cleaned regularly as well as the laser lens. The light shield tends to trap soot and smoke and negatively impact the clarity of the lens. An air assist can help keep the air circulating around the lens.

When cleaning the light shield or the laser head, disconnect the power from the machine. Use alcohol on a lint-free cloth or paper towel to clean the inner and outer surfaces of the shield. Use an alcohol-soaked cotton swab to clean the laser lens and the cross-hair sight. A helpful video can be viewed at https://youtu.be/lh53_cg6tW0.

Lubrication of the steel shafts is critical to preventing rust and maintaining the smooth travel of the x-axis wheels. For these purposes xTool includes a small container of grease in the assembly kit package (FIG. 18).

FIG. 18. Super Lube, recommended for use on the xTool D1, is a multi-purpose, safe, synthetic lubricant. Due to some shipping limitations it may not be included with all assembly kits. It is available from Amazon at https://amzn.to/35vpwIT. Credit: Amazon

The tension on the belts is a critical setting. If the belts are too loose they will cause deformation of the engraved or cut pattern. Tightening the belts, although an uncommon need, is easily done with an Allen wrench.

Contact: Shenzhen MakerWorks Technology Co., LTD, Maker Works Technology Inc., 16035 Arrow Hwy., Irwindale, CA 91706, https://www.xtool.com, xTool Customer Service: vicky@xtool.com.

7. xTool M1

The xTool M1 (FIG. 1), introduced in the spring of 2022, represents the first true desktop creative workstation, able to engrave and cut the widest selection of craft materials ever. The M1 is truly unique, with a dual cutting head that incorporates both a 10W laser module (also available as a 5W model) and a precision soft material cutting blade, both housed in a single precision laser head module.

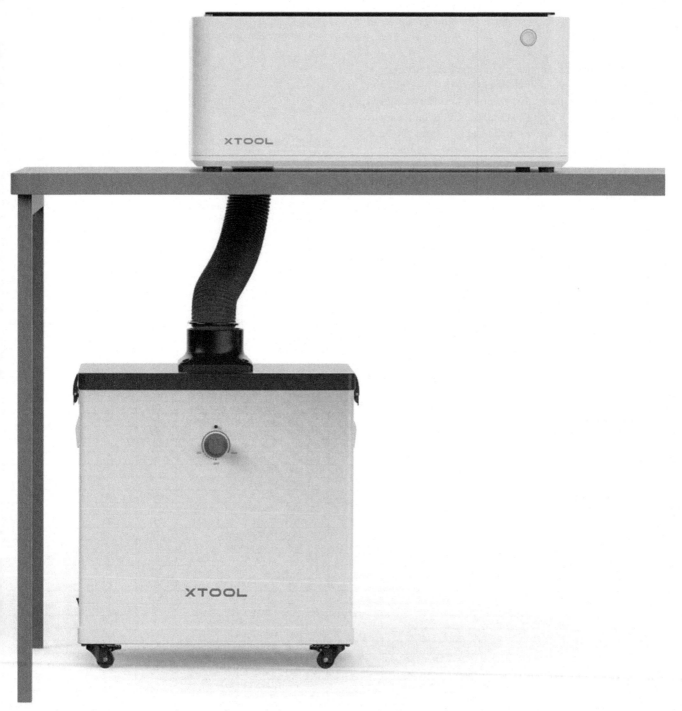

FIG. 1. The xTool M1 creative workstation, along with the xTool Smoke Purifier, form an integrated system that streamlines the production workflow with automatic focusing, built-in workpiece settings, and much more. Credit: xTool

The M1 represents a new generation of laser engraver/cutter, one that is more focused on creative activities, as opposed to testing and experimentation. This new generation is cleaner, safer, more accessible, and ultimately, more productive.

The xTool M1, as well as the xTool D1, are 2022 recipients of the esteemed Red Dot Design awards (red-dot.org) in recognition of their world-class creative design features. The M1 is a sleek, modern self-contained unit touting a feature list heretofore unavailable.

The incorporation of a cutting blade greatly expands the range of materials that can be processed, adding vinyl. Vinyl cannot be cut with a laser due to the release of chlorine gas, which is toxic to humans, and harmful to machine parts. The addition of the cutting blade, similar in function to the Silhouette and Cricut blade-cutting machines, enables the user to produce signs, logos, t-shirts, and other products, all without odor or burnt edges.

The M1 is one of only a small number of self-contained laser engraver/cutters on the market; the first diode laser device of its kind; and the only hybrid machine available. The combination of its technical capabilities and price make it a truly unique machine, and a smart value. The benefit of an enclosure, to shield the user from the inevitable hazards of the strong laser light, and air-borne contaminants, is considerable. Entry-level open-frame laser engraver/cutters do not include an enclosure, the cost of which can approach the cost of the engraver/cutter itself!

The xTool M1 also has what is perhaps the most valuable, if not the most useful feature of any creative craft machine: availability of manufacturer testing results on a wide selection of materials. xTool has meticulously tested hundreds of materials, recording the results of their experimentation and releasing it to users (FIG. 2). In addition, the Materials Parameters for Reference sheet lists the actual power, speed, and pass settings for dozens of readily available materials (FIG. 3). Knowledge of the optimum machine settings for a laser engraver/cutter is akin to finding hidden treasure.

MATERIAL REPORT LIST #5
WOOD

*THE ACTUAL RESULTS MAY DIFFER DUE TO THE FACT THAT VARIOUS BRANDS OF PLYWOODS MAY CONTAIN DIFFERENT NUMBERS OF LAYERS, WHICH CAN CAUSE CHANGES IN THE CUTTING EFFICIENCY.

This document contains all wood materials that M1 has been testing so far. All provided information includes material name, whether it used Laser or Blade, to cut or engrave, thickness, machine module, Pass, and result.

Please note that:
- We are still testing and optimizing the features of M1, the testing data may change due to the machine's optimization.

We will continue uploading our test reports on different types of materials in the future. Stay tuned with us!

Material Name	Laser/Blade	Cut/Engrave	Thickness	Module	Pass	Result
Wood, Aspen Plywood 3.0 mm	Laser	Cut	3mm	5W	2	SUCCESS
Wood, Aspen Plywood 3.0 mm	Laser	Raster Engrave	3mm	5W	1	SUCCESS
Wood, Aspen Plywood 3.0 mm	Laser	Vector Engrave	3mm	5W	1	SUCCESS
Wood, Aspen Plywood 3.0 mm	Laser	Cut	3mm	10W	1	SUCCESS
Wood, Aspen Plywood 3.0 mm	Laser	Raster Engrave	3mm	10W	1	SUCCESS
Wood, Aspen Plywood 3.0 mm	Laser	Vector Engrave	3mm	10W	1	SUCCESS
Wood, Aspen Plywood Sheet 1.7 mm	Laser	Cut	1.7mm	5W	1	Fail
Wood, Aspen Plywood Sheet 1.7 mm	Laser	Raster Engrave	1.7mm	5W	1	SUCCESS
Wood, Aspen Plywood Sheet 1.7 mm	Laser	Vector Engrave	1.7mm	5W	1	SUCCESS
Wood, Aspen Plywood Sheet 1.7 mm	Laser	Cut	1.7mm	10W	1	Fail
Wood, Aspen Plywood Sheet 1.7 mm	Laser	Raster Engrave	1.7mm	10W	1	SUCCESS
Wood, Aspen Plywood Sheet 1.7 mm	Laser	Vector Engrave	1.7mm	10W	1	SUCCESS
Wood, Balsa Plywood 13.0 mm	Laser	Cut	13mm	5W	6	SUCCESS
Wood, Balsa Plywood 13.0 mm	Laser	Raster Engrave	13mm	5W	1	SUCCESS
Wood, Balsa Plywood 13.0 mm	Laser	Vector Engrave	13mm	5W	1	SUCCESS
Wood, Balsa Plywood 13.0 mm	Laser	Cut	13mm	10W	5	SUCCESS
Wood, Balsa Plywood 13.0 mm	Laser	Raster Engrave	13mm	10W	1	SUCCESS
Wood, Balsa Plywood 13.0 mm	Laser	Vector Engrave	13mm	10W	1	SUCCESS

FIG. 2 This is one of the many material testing reports produced for the xTool M1.

xTool M1(10W) Materials parameters for reference

Material code	Material name	Machine	Processing mode	Power %	Speed mm/s	Processing times
AE001	Rubber mat for engraving	M1 10W	Laser vector engraving	70	50	1
AE001	Rubber mat for engraving	M1 10W	Laser bitmap engraving	100	40	2
AH001	PU Heat transfer film	M1 10W	Tool cutting	90	80	1
AH002	PET Heat transfer film	M1 10W	Tool cutting	105	80	1
AH003	PVC Heat transfer film	M1 10W	Tool cutting	60	80	1
AL001	PU artificial leather	M1 10W	Tool cutting			
AL006	Gray top-layer leather	M1 10W	Tool cutting			
AL016	PU artificial leather with knit fabric	M1 10W	Tool cutting	190	80	1
AP017	PVC self-adhesive lettering film	M1 10W	Tool cutting	75	80	1
AP024	Kraft paper 200g	M1 10W	Tool cutting	234	80	1
AP038	White self-adhesive material	M1 10W	Tool cutting	78	80	1
APL0010	Black acrylic 3.0mm	M1 10W	Tool cutting	100	4	2
APL0010	Black acrylic 3.0mm	M1 10W	Laser vector engraving	50	50	1
APL0010	Black acrylic 3.0mm	M1 10W	Laser bitmap engraving	100	60	1
APL054	PVC colored transparent sheet	M1 10W	Tool cutting	347	80	3
APL055	PVC frosted transparent sheet	M1 10W	Tool cutting	379	80	4
AW050	Basswood plywood 3mm (launched by xTool)	M1 10W	Tool cutting	100	4	1
AW050	Basswood plywood 3mm (launched by xTool)	M1 10W	Laser bitmap engraving	70	175	1
AW051	Black Walnut (launched by xTool)	M1 10W	Tool cutting	100	4	1
AW051	Black Walnut (launched by xTool)	M1 10W	Laser bitmap engraving	70	175	1
AW069	Materials library_Black Walnut plywood (30cm × 30cm) 2pcs	M1 10W	Tool cutting	100	4	1
AW069	Materials library_Black Walnut plywood (30cm × 30cm) 2pcs	M1 10W	Laser vector engraving	60	40	1
AW069	Materials library_Black Walnut plywood (30cm × 30cm) 2pcs	M1 10W	Laser bitmap engraving	70	70	1
AW070	Materials library_Pine plywood (30cm × 30cm) 2pcs	M1 10W	Tool cutting	100	4	1
AW070	Materials library_Pine plywood (30cm × 30cm) 2pcs	M1 10W	Laser vector engraving	90	40	1
AW070	Materials library_Pine plywood (30cm × 30cm) 2pcs	M1 10W	Laser bitmap engraving	80	60	1
AW073	Materials library_M... wood (30cm × 3...	M1 10W	...cutting			

FIG. 3. This list of dozens of materials, along with their M1 machine settings was generated during lab testing of the M1 prototype machine. Similar information, available at https://www.xtool.com/pages/material-settings, ensures that users will be able to produce acceptable, repeatable, results, without the time-consuming testing requirements.

Safety

The M1 has been designed to provide a safe working environment. The working heads are totally enclosed, shielding the operator from the intense light of the laser. The machine lid has been engineered with an auto-stop feature that ceases the operation of the machine when the lid is opened. If either the laser or the blade have been in operation, they stop immediately when the lid is lifted.

Despite the fact that all moving parts are contained in the M1 enclosure, and that opening the enclosure will halt operation, it is recommended that children, of any age, only use the device under the supervision of an adult. That being said, the M1, along with the optional xTool Smoke Purifier, makes it possible to bring laser engraving and cutting out of the basement, garage, and workshop, and into the home studio, without the need for external venting nor modification of a living space.*

As the machine is used, the built-in ventilation fan discharges odors and toxic gases into the optional xTool Smoke Purifier for treatment, leaving the work environment safe and virtually odor-free. As previously stated, the air purifier makes it possible to use the M1 inside a home, and has been certified by the Federal Communications Commission and Conformite Europeenne. Inside the M1, a fan above the laser head works to disperse work particles and smoke from the work surface, to protect the lens, and essentially serve as an air assist.

Assembly and Maintenance

The xTool M1 is shipped assembled, except for the smoke exhaust pipe. Over time, the cutting blade will need replacement based on the amount of time it has been used, and the composition of the materials it has cut. Like any laser engraver, the laser head will be susceptible to errant smoke and air-borne contaminants, and will need to be cleaned routinely with a cotton swab dipped in alcohol. The chrome-plated optical shaft will need to be lubricated with grease (https://amzn.to/3yFIPM3) on a regular basis, anywhere from every 15 days to two months, depending on use, to prevent rust and ensure optimal performance.

Size & Weight

The M1 is quite compact, fitting easily on a small table or counter. Its outside dimensions are 22" x 18" x 9", with an actual inside workspace of 15" x 12". The weight is 21.6 lbs.

Connectivity

The xTool M1 can be controlled by a Mac or Windows computer using either a direct USB cable connection, or WiFi (FIG. 4).

Compatibility with LightBurn

LightBurn software can be used with the M1 with some limitations. The software will only work with the laser-processing component of the device, not the blade-cutting functions, and requires that compatible files, or native G-code be imported to the M1 manually. No other software, other than the proprietary xTool Creative Space, provided by xTool, will work. According to xTool, the Creative Space software will add significant capabilities over time.

A small room may need the benefit of a window exhaust fan to remove any lingering odors. Some workpieces, dependent on their composition, may retain a lingering burnt smell after processing.

FIG. 4. Connecting the M1 to a computer is fast and easy. The inset in the lower right shows that the M1 is connected.

Focusing

Proper focusing is always a critical step in the production workflow for any laser-processed workpiece. The M1 can automatically adjust the focus based on a ring code adhered to xTool-supplied materials (FIG. 5). If the material is user-supplied, the M1 uses AI to compute the thickness of the material, anywhere from 0 to 16mm, and automatically enter that value in the software to adjust the focus both for engraving and cutting (FIG. 6).

FIG. 5. A ring code is provided on all xTool-supplied materials to provide the M1 with relevant information regarding material characteristics and processing requirements. Ultimately it will be replaced with a standard QR code.

FIG. 6. Here a flat rock has been placed on the workbed. The red spot that appears in the center of the rock is the laser that is determining its thickness by using the Auto-measure button in the Creative Space software (inset).

Accuracy and Strength.

The FAC lens configuration, which maintains high beam quality, generates a laser spot size of 0.08 x 0.08mm, producing an ultra-fine engraving precision of 0.01mm. The laser head incorporates dual laser technology, focusing two diode lasers into one spot, producing a laser intensity sufficiently strong to cut 8mm basswood in a single pass. The image resolution is an impressive 500 dpi.

Smart Camera.

The M1 is provided with a 16MP high-resolution camera to aid in visual processing. After loading a workpiece in the M1, the user can remain at their computer and see the processing stages as captured by the camera. This capability provides exceptional control over the placement of the image onto the work surface of the substrate, ensuring that the image size, angle, and orientation, are accurate.

Image Extraction

The M1 is able to capture graphic designs, images, and drawings from any flat hand-drawn or printed surface and import them into the M1 software for modification or refinement. In lieu of a flatbed scanner, the user can create hand-drawn artwork, or appropriate two-dimensional images from virtually any source that they are authorized to use, and place the material on the M1 work bed. The built-in high-resolution camera captures the images, displays them on the Creative Space canvas, and allows the user to edit, crop, resize, re-orient, and position the image onto a substrate for processing.

Batch Processing

Based on the shape of multiple workpieces, the AI system can determine how to process defined functions for the entire batch, all at one time. The user simply defines the placement of an image on one of a number of like-sized shapes. Using the Smart fill button, the Creative Space software intelligently determines the location of each workpiece, and based on all necessary factors, places the same image on each one, properly sized and positioned.

Creative Space Software

The xTool Creative Space interface, although basic, provides a good selection of options for imaginative expression. On start-up the user sees an image of the work area as captured by the built-in high-resolution camera and displayed on the on-screen canvas. The user places their workpiece onto the device working area. If the material is xTool-branded, the ring code on the material will automatically set the focus; if the material is user-supplied, the user sets the material in the work area and presses the Auto-measure button to set the focus (FIG. 7). With a minimum of effort, and the calculation of a few settings, the user can be producing their creations quickly and efficiently (FIG. 8).

FIG. 7. In the work area the user has placed a piece of aluminum foil, shiny side up, to prevent stray laser movement from hitting the laser bed and leaving an unwanted image. The text tool has been used to type the word "Creativity," with the user's choice of typeface. The user positions the word in the required position and selects the Engrave option.

FIG. 8. This stone was engraved without the use of any pre-treatment. After processing the user has the option of adding color to improve the contrast of the lettering.

The Creative Space interface consists mainly of two toolbars, one vertical and one horizontal, that are in proximity to the workspace canvas. The vertical toolbar deals mainly with the creation of elements that will ultimately be output. The tools include:

- The Import button, which leads to accessing one or more files for processing, and setting their properties.
- The Insert button that creates lines, rectangles, and circles.
- The Shape tool that provides a palette of dozens of unique shapes, such as stars, arrows, gears, and dozens of primitive forms that can be combined or modified using other Creative Space tools (FIG. 9).
- The Text tool that provides an input window, defaulting with the words "Your text here," in which text is entered, a typeface is selected, and optional intercharacter spacing can be applied. The handles that appear around the text can be used to condense, expand, enlarge, reduce, or rotate the text.
- The Vector tool that supports the drawing of a vector path. Any of the anchor points can be double-clicked once to convert them into a rounded corner with adjustable curvature, or double-clicked twice to convert them back to a sharp corner.
- The Extract tool that can acquire an image that has been captured by the M1's camera, edit that image with the Magic wand, Eraser, and Crop tools, and then use it for processing on a workpiece.

The Creative Space horizontal toolbar presents tools that interact with images that have been imported or created directly in the workspace. These include:

- Undo, which cancels the last action.
- Redo, which reinstates the last action.
- Outline, which traces the outline of an image including the inner and outer outline.
- Array, which creates a grid or circular duplication of an image.
- Smart fill, which is a "magical" feature that enables the user to duplicate a design they have created on a single material, automatically on a number of like materials laid out in a random fashion. The software makes the design conform in the proper size and orientation of the original.
- Align, which forces two or more elements to align or distribute to a prescribed position.
- Arrange, which changes the stacking order of two or more elements to the front or back, or forward or backward.
- Combine, which supports the use of two or more shapes to either unite, subtract, unite at overlap, or subtract at overlap, to produce a new shape composed of parts of the original shapes.
- Reflect, which will produce a duplicate of a selected element in a horizontal or vertical reflected duplicate.
- Position, which displays the x and y coordinates of a selected element, with 0,0 indicating the upper left corner. The user can enter new coordinates which will change the position of the element.
- Size, which shows the width and height of the selected element in the unit system defined by the user.
- Rotate, which shows the angle of rotation of the selected element.
- Zoom, which enlarges or decreases the view of the work area, with a minimum size of 25% and a maximum of 1000%.

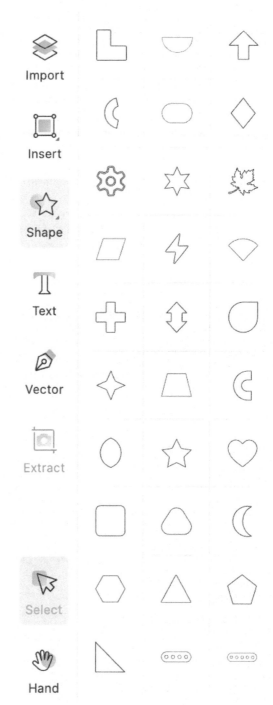

FIG. 9. *The variety of shapes available in the Shape tool ensures that the user can quickly construct or modify an outline suitable for a given task.*

FIG. 10. *The four main M1 machine modes.*

The M1 has four main work modes, or processing types: Laser flat, Laser cylindrical, Open plane, and Blade cut (FIG. 10). The Laser flat mode is the typical workflow for most flat materials, and does not involve removing the floor plate on the bottom of the machine, which can lift off with the removal of five screws. The Laser cylindrical workflow involves the use of the Rotary Attachment, and requires that the metal floor plate, or baseplate, be removed, and the entire machine be elevated using a set of risers. The Open plane workflow also requires the removal of the metal floor plate, and that the entire machine be positioned over a workpiece that is too large to fit inside the M1 enclosure. Finally, the Blade cut workflow involves the use of the cutting blade positioned over a cutting mat with the work material adhered to the mat surface.

Materials that are processed with the cutting blade are first adhered to a cutting mat, to hold them in place. There are two varieties of cutting mat; the red one which has a high-grip adhesive surface for fabric, and the blue one which has a low-grip adhesive surface for paper and vinyl (FIG. 11). Each mat is provided with two sheets of protective film, one on each side. Removing the front protective film reveals the adhesive surface. The protective film should be replaced after each use to maintain the strength of the adhesive layer.

FIG. 11. The adhesive surface on the cutting mat is covered with a sheet of protective film when not in use.

The selection of the material, specified in the Material window, will automatically determine the machine settings for laser-processing. If the material has been sourced from xTool, the software will automatically use the material's associated ring code settings for Power, Speed, and Pass. Should the user want to override the recommended settings they can enter their own by selecting the "User-defined parameters" option. If the material is actually User-defined, the operator must input the necessary settings manually, although they may be based on the settings suggested for a comparable xTool material.

The associated parameters for xTool sourced materials will change based on the ultimate type of processing to be performed, and the type of material to be used. Laser processing modes include: Score, Engrave, or Cut; Blade cut has the single option of Cut. The score setting produces an engraved outline of the full vector image, the engrave setting produces a solid engraving of the object, and the cut setting, cuts out the object.

The M1 processes both bitmap (scan line-by-scan line) and vector (trajectory path) files. Bitmaps can be altered using the Grid filter, to alter its pixelization, and the blur and sharpening options to affect its appearance.

Laser cut materials can benefit from being lifted up slightly off the baseplate, in order to allow air to circulate below, and let smoke escape from the bottom of the material. This is typically the function of a honeycomb panel. The M1 solution, provided with the machine, is the use of ten triangular prisms, 12-inch aluminum rods that can be placed across the baseplate to raise the workpiece. The prisms have proven to reduce soot and smoke discoloration (FIG. 12).

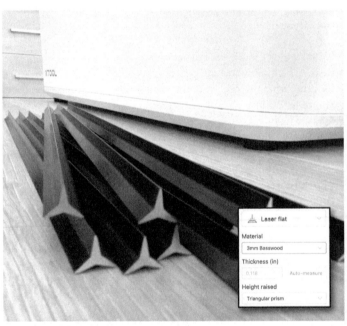

FIG. 12. The set of triangular prisms provides an effective way to raise a workpiece off of the baseplate, enabling air circulation, and therefore removing smoke, and minimizing discoloration. The inset in the lower right corner shows that the height of the material has been raised to account for the use of the triangular prisms.

The materials listed for laser processing in the initial version of the software include: 3mm Basswood, 3.5mm Cardboard, Walnut Plywood, Black Acrylic, Stainless Steel Dog Tag, Metal Card, Laser engraved rubber mat, Mahogany Plywood, Rock Coaster, and Cherry Plywood. The materials listed for blade cutting include: PU Heat Transfer Vinyl, White Sticker Paper, PU Leather, Colored Glossy PVC Sheet, Transparent Frosted PVC, Kraft Paper, and Self-adhesive PVC Sheet. Any blade cutting operation requires the use of a vector file.

The session content can be imported from a file or image, can be lifted from a drawing or print placed inside the M1, or can be designed directly within the program. The tools provided to edit an imported image are limited to resizing, rotating, reflecting (horizontally or vertically), magic wand, eraser, and cropping. An original design can be created using a variety of shapes, text elements, and vector paths.

Elements that will be scored appear on-screen in an orange outline; elements that will be engraved appear in a solid orange; and elements that will be cut appear in a purple outline (FIG. 13).

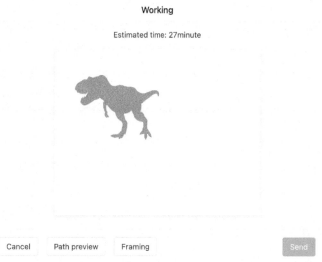

Working

Estimated time: 27minute

Cancel   Path preview   Framing   Send

FIG. 14. The Working window provides the user with the options to preview the laser head path, view the framing of the image, cancel the process, or send the job to the M1.

FIG. 13. The laser processing status of an object is indicated by its color: orange outline for Score, orange solid for Engrave, and purple outline for Cut.

Working

Press the button on xTool M1 to start processing.

To avoid fire risk

Handle flammable materials with care

Do not leave the device unattended when it is working.

Cancel

FIG. 15. The job will not be processed until the user presses the flashing blue button on the M1.

After the material has been positioned, the elements and/or images have been set, the parameters have been entered, the actual processing is initiated by pressing the Start button. The Working window is presented with an estimate of the processing time, and options to preview the path of the imager and to show how the image will be framed. If the operator approves, the job is sent to the M1 using the Send button (FIG. 14). The job is not processed until the user physically goes to the M1 and presses the button in the front upper right corner of the machine. This final step is a precaution to remind the operator that there is always a fire risk, and that the machine must be monitored closely at all times when in operation (FIG. 15).

The Creative Space software is unique in many regards, perhaps the most significant of which is the Projects Center option (FIG. 16), which presents an ever-increasing display of comprehensive plans for various categories of objects, sorted by laser device (M1, D1, or both), difficulty level (1, 2, or 3), processing type (laser engrave, laser cut, blade cut), and material type (wood, metal, leather, etc.). When a project is selected, the user sees the material required and has the option to buy it directly from the xTool website (FIG. 17). From this point the user can directly start the project from the main software user interface (FIG. 18).

In addition to the Projects Center link, the Creative Space interface provides direct access to Support and Shop links. The support link takes the user directly to support documents, as well as a Contact Us link to submit a help request to the support team. The shop link takes the user to the xTool website with direct access to purchase materials as well as accessories.

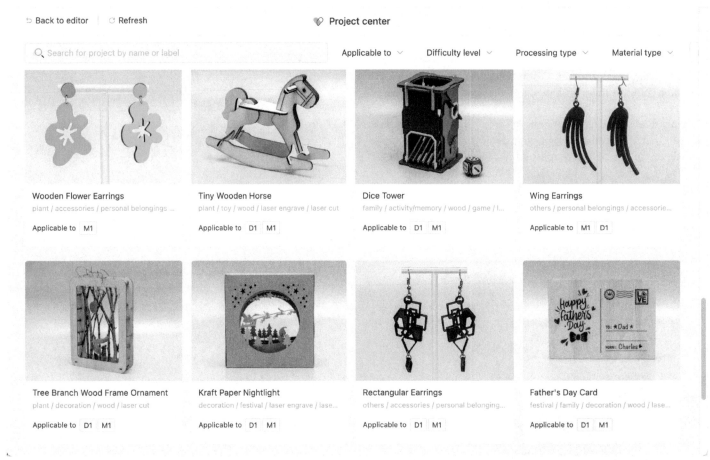

FIG. 16. *From within the Creative Space software the user can select from a variety of projects, with immediate access to the necessary file(s) to create it.*

FIG. 17. *Selecting a project leads to this screen, showing a description, a list of materials, a link to the xTool on-line store, and a button to load the project file into Creative Space.*

FIG. 18. *The actual project file immediately appears in the Creative Space user interface.*

8. Prep and Finishing Laser-Processed Materials*

Although many items exit the laser engraver/cutter bed ready-to-use, most require some form of finishing or prior preparation. These steps will be in addition to those covered in the Pre/Post Surface Treatments chapter. Using a variety of relatively low-cost equipment the user can establish a successful production workflow that addresses most of the likely problems and concerns.

Measuring

The first step in dealing with a new material is to learn as much as possible about its physical properties. In the case of laser engraving and cutting a critical factor is the material thickness. An ordinary ruler, with 1/32" increments, may be accurate enough to determine thickness, however, an easier and more precise method is with a digital caliper (FIG. 1). A precision caliper is typically accurate to within 0.01 mm, or +/-0.0005 inches. Digital calipers can usually convert between inches, millimeters, and fractions, and measure both inside and outside dimensions.

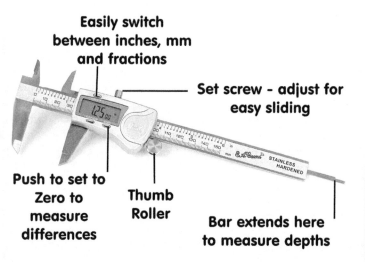

Easily switch between inches, mm and fractions

Set screw - adjust for easy sliding

Push to set to Zero to measure differences

Thumb Roller

Bar extends here to measure depths

FIG. 1. Digital Vernier Caliper Measuring Tool. Credit: Amazon.

The outside jaws of the caliper are used to measure the thickness of a material; an indicator of whether or not a particular laser cutter can penetrate its depth and produce a clean cut. The inside jaws can be used to measure the inside width of a circular or rectangular cut, in order to replicate its size. Care must be taken to insure that the caliper is clean and free of dust and dirt to confidently make accurate readings. The same is true for the material being measured.

To begin a measurement the outside jaws must be closed, and the digital display set to zero. The jaws should be closed on the material so that there is a bit of a drag, but not closed to the extent that it bites into the surface.

Cutting and Trimming

Materials destined for laser engraving are seldom available in the pre-cut sizes that a user may need for specific jobs. Although materials are generally sold in convenient sizes, they are often too big for a specific purpose, and therefore must be cut or trimmed. In certain circumstances the laser itself can be used to cut oversize material, but this is often at the expense of time, and comes with the inevitable resultant singed cut edges.

Materials can be purchased from local or on-line sources, cut-to-size. While this may be convenient, it is most likely more expensive and certainly more time-consuming. The obvious answer is to do the cutting in-house.

Depending on the thickness of the material, whether paper, cardboard, or wood, it may be cut by using a self-healing cutting mat (FIG. 2), a steel ruler with an edge guard (FIG. 3), or a t-square (FIG. 4), and a utility knife (FIG. 5). The cutting mat protects the surface that it sits on and offers a surface that the user can cut into, to insure that the piece they are cutting is completely cut through. The mat also serves to keep the blade sharp by offering little resistance.

FIG. 2. Breman Precision Self-Healing Cutting Mat 24x36 Inches. Credit: Amazon.

To begin, the user should lightly draw a line on the material representing the cut. This serves as a guide, should the ruler or t-square move, even slightly. The material is aligned to guidelines on the mat, and if a t-square is used, the head of the t-square should be flush against a side of the mat.

*Items listed in this chapter can be purchased on Amazon.com. The links are provided here: **https://tinyurl.com/3s8sxbkm** and may generate a small commission.*

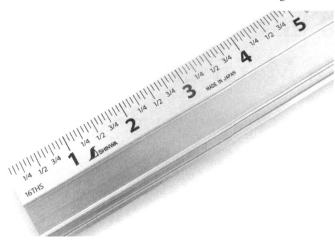

FIG. 3. Shinwa 24" Extruded Aluminum Cutting Rule Ruler Gauge with Non slip rubber Backing. Credit: Amazon.

FIG. 4. Ludwig Precision Heavy-Duty Aluminum T-Square,, 24-inch. Credit: Amazon.

FIG. 5. WorkPro Folding Utility Knife Quick-change Box Cutter. Credit: Amazon.

Safety is very important, and the user should be sure that the piece being cut is secure on the mat, that the ruler is securely pressed against the material in the proper place, and that the knife blade is sharp. The knife is sharp enough to cause a bad finger cut, so exercise every precaution. The blade should protrude no more than about 2cm. Extending the blade too far makes it wobble, makes the cut uneven, as well as makes the cutter less controllable and therefore more dangerous.

The user moves the blade from the top of the piece in several firm movements downward toward the body, until the cut is complete. If the piece being cut is longer than the ruler, the user should complete the cut almost to the end of the ruler, keeping the blade against the cut edge, then slide the ruler downward carefully so that it is aligned with the first cut.

The thicker the material, the more scores that the knife will have to make, and possibly, the less precise and clean the cut. The objective is to always let the knife do the work. Although thicker materials can be cut using this method, there is a practical limit.

Thinner materials, such as paper and card stock can be cut with a rotary or guillotine trimmer (FIG. 6), or with a scissor, provided that a straight line has been drawn as a guide.

FIG. 6. Swingline Paper Cutter, Guillotine Trimmer, 15" Cut Length, 10 Sheet Capacity, ClassicCut Lite (9315). Credit: Amazon.

Manually Cutting Acrylic. Acrylic is not easy to cut by hand since it is highly prone to scratching and cracking. New sheets come with a protective adhesive cover, which provides surface protection. Off-cuts should be covered with masking tape, or painter's tape, to protect edges that could be damaged. Larger surface areas can be covered with paper and held in position with tape. The acrylic should be placed on a self-healing mat and held in place with a rigid steel ruler incorporating an edge guard to protect the hand holding it in place. A line should be drawn indicating the location of the cut. If the acrylic is particularly thick, the piece should be clamped to a worksurface, holding the straight edge, with the piece to be cut off extending off of the work surface. The line is gently but firmly scored using an acrylic scoring tool (FIG. 7), holding the tool tightly against the ruler edge. This motion is repeated until the material has been cut.

FIG. 7. Red Devil 1170 Plexiglass cutting tool. Credit: Amazon.

Inexperienced users should avoid trying to cut thick acrylic since doing so can result in stress fractures in the material and rough edges. Scoring and snapping the material is also not advisable for the same reasons.

Small Cuts. Occasionally the laser cutter only partially cuts through a given piece of material, leaving a portion still connected to the workpiece. It is usually difficult to determine if a laser cut has been completed while the material is on the laser bed, and once removed it is nearly impossible to reposition it, and attempt another pass. A solution is to use a hobby knife (FIG. 8) to carefully follow the outline of the partial cut with successive scores, until it is cut through.

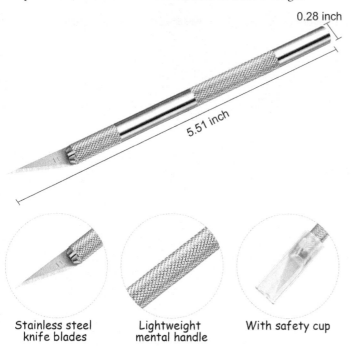

FIG. 9. Marshalltown17" Tile Cutter, Perfect for Porcelain, Ceramic, Glass, and Mosaic Tile. Credit: Amazon.

FIG. 8. 15 Packs Hobby Knife Precision Knife Set, Stainless Steel Precision Cutter. Credit: Amazon.

Tile/Glass Cutting. While many kinds of ceramic, porcelain, and glass are available in convenient pre-cut sizes, there are circumstances where a piece will need to be cut smaller. There are many specialized bench saws that can do the job, however a convenient and inexpensive solution for straight cuts is the use of a manual two-rod rail system tile cutter (FIG. 9). In use, the target piece is marked with the cut position, and placed on the bed of the cutter against the front guide. The cut mark is positioned below where the tungsten carbide scoring wheel, guided by the handle, will run up the length of the tile, while exerting slight pressure. The piece is scored bottom-to-top, just once. The pressure toggle plate, also attached to the handle, is positioned on the tile, and the handle is pressed downward exerting pressure on the tile and causing it to break cleanly on the scored line.

Tabletop Machine Cutting. The best, fastest, and most accurate way to cut materials for laser engraving/cutting is with a tabletop power saw. The performance of the saw, the accuracy of the cut, and the smoothness of the cut edges is dependent on the power of the saw motor and the proper selection of the blade. Many table saws are overpowered for this purpose, however, we have found the Rockwell Bladerunner X2 to be a good fit (FIG. 10).

The Rockwell Bladerunner X2 has a small footprint, about the size of the Ortur Laser Master Pro 2. Despite its small size it is capable of cutting a wide variety of materials, with rip, cross, and scroll cuts, rivaling much larger table saws. Its versatility is due to its quick set-up rip fence, with two easy lock screws, scribed increment saw

FIG. 10. Rockwell RK7323 BladeRunner X2 Portable Tabletop Saw with Steel Rip Fence, Miter Gauge and 7 Accessories. Credit: Amazon.

bed markers, and a fast blade change mechanism. The selection of available blades, for wood, ceramic, plastic, aluminum, and metal, ensures that it will be able to cut virtually any material that is suitable for laser processing, and do so with professional results.

No less important than performance are the machine's safety features. The large on/off safety switch is easy to access for an immediate stop. Blades can be changed without the need for tools. The blade shield supports the attachment of a vacuum hose to connect to a shop vac, to remove saw dust and material shavings immediately, and leave a clear view of the blade cutting area.

Burnishing, Scrapping, Picking and Weeding
There are circumstances when blue painter's tape or craft transfer tape, both with adhesive backing, are used to protect the surface of a wood workpiece. These materials are secured to the wood using a plastic scraper that eliminates air pockets and wrinkles, and insures a tight adhesion. The tape, being very thin, and easily burned, yields to

the heat of the laser, while protecting the surface area that is not exposed to the laser. The tape barrier can help to prevent the formation of charring and discoloration, and can also serve as a mask for adding color or post-laser treating.

A problem arises after imaging, when the tape needs to be removed. Depending on the intricacies of image, there may be extremely small pieces of tape remaining that cannot easily be peeled off by hand. In such cases a sharply pointed instrument called a weeding tool (FIG. 11) can be quite effective.

Another method involves adhering a piece of tape with greater tack, burnishing it over the remaining stray bits of tape, and lifting them off.

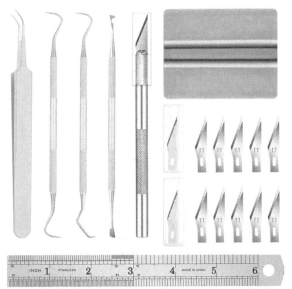

FIG. 11. 17 Pack Weeding Craft Tool with Scraper, Hook, Spatula, and Tweezers. Credit: Amazon.

Drilling

Making holes for keychains, luggage tags, ornaments and other items needing to be hung or attached, can usually be accomplished using the cutting function of the laser. For whatever reason, that function might not have been performed, and needs to be done after the item has been engraved.

The most convenient way to drill holes in a wide variety of materials is with a small rotary tool, such as the Dremel (FIG. 12). The rotary tool can accommodate a variety of drill sizes, and using a compatible drill stand (FIG. 13), can make precision holes quickly.

FIG. 12. Dremel Lite 7760 N/10 4V Li-Ion Cordless Rotary Tool, Variable Rotary Tool Kit, USB Charging, Credit: Amazon.

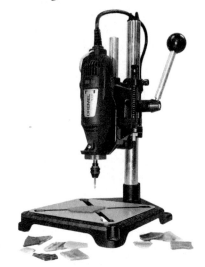

FIG. 13. Milescraft 1097 ToolStand - Drill Press Stand (compatible with Dremel). Credit: Amazon.

Sanding

Material surface imperfections, usually in wood, appear as rough or irregular areas that can be seen visually, or felt by touch. Soft woods are particularly susceptible to nicks and scratches that may even be accentuated by laser engraving. Regardless of their source, imperfections on the surface and edges of workpieces must be eliminated prior to engraving or cutting. Also, keep in mind that sanding may be necessary after laser engraving and cutting, to address various finishing operations (see Pre/Post Surface Treatments, page 82).

The choice of a sander should include features such as variable speed, in order to maintain control over the precise amount of abrasion being applied (FIG. 14). A dust collection attachment is a requirement, both to keep the dust off of the workpiece and to keep it out of the air, and protect the user. A sandpaper system that uses hook-and-loop makes changing the sandpaper quick, and ensures that it stays in position while in use.

FIG. 14. DEWALT Random Orbit Sander, Variable Speed, 5-Inch (DWE6423). Credit: Amazon.

The choice of sandpaper grit will depend on the characteristics of the workpiece. In general, a 220 grit sandpaper is a good starting point.

The size of a workpiece, either as a pre-processed or completed laser cut piece, may be relatively small, and may have intricate cut edges, curves, slots, recesses, and cut-outs, all of which may be too small for a normal-size sander. In such cases a precision pen-size sander (FIG. 15), with a linear rather than rotary motion, may be useful. The sander comes with a variety of small changeable straight and angled shanks that can fit in tight spaces. Each shank can accommodate a like-sized adhesive piece of sandpaper available in a variety of grits.

FIG. 15. Proxxon 28594 Pen Sander PS 13, 12 Volt. Credit: Amazon.

The Dremel rotary tool has a reputation for accommodating a wide variety of attachments, including many sanding attachments. Although it is not as narrow nor as light as a pen sander, the Dremel can sand many hard-to-reach spaces. An advantage of the Dremel is the fact that it can used while it is mounted in its drill press stand wherein the workpiece can be moved while the rotary tool remains in a fixed position.

The sanding operation may require more serious attention if the workpiece is large, and/or the surface is particularly rough. The WEN 6502T with a 4.3 amp, ½ HP motor, contains two sanding surfaces: one a 4" x 36" adjustable belt sander that can tilt from 0 to 90 degrees; and the second, a 6" disc sander with an adjustable support table and miter gauge (FIG. 15). The machine accommodates a wide variety of sanding grits, each of which can be changed quickly and easily. Both sanding options are mounted in a solid cast iron base, providing a stable and secure sanding surface with a minimum of vibration. The unit includes a 2.25" dust collection port for attaching an optional vacuum system.

Vacuuming

Any operation that involves sanding or cutting will produce dust. A clean work environment is a major protection against fire, with the added benefit of removing pollutants from the air, and therefore protecting the health of the people working there.

A hand-held cordless vacuum cleaner (FIG. 17) is a handy tool to clean up loose debris and remove it from the environment. It can be used not only to clean work surfaces, including the laser bed, but to remove surface dirt and dust directly from workpieces prior to, and after, sanding.

FIG. 17 BLACK+DECKER dustbuster Handheld Vacuum, Cordless, 16V (CHV1410L). Credit: Amazon.

Painting

Airbrushing. An airbrush (FIG. 18) can work in concert with a laser engraver/cutter in a number of ways. The first, and perhaps the most obvious, is that it can replace the need for spray cans for applying a number of surface treatments to materials, before and/or after engraving or cutting. One such treatment is the application of white spray paint for the creation of engraved photos on ceramic tile, commonly known as the Norton Method, or the Norton White Tile Method (NWT). The method works due to the reaction of the laser with the Titanium Dioxide ($TIO2$) in the paint (FIG. 19). Titanium dioxide is a synthetic white pigment that provides maximum whiteness and opacity in paint. When the laser hits the coating it turns the paint black, and adheres permanently to the surface. Users can buy Titanium Dioxide, mix it with alcohol (1ml TIO2 to 10ml alcohol), and apply it using an airbrush. (See Pre/Post Surface Treatments, page 82).

FIG. 15 The WEN 6502T belt disc sander brings considerable power to the sanding operation, eliminating jagged edges and splinters, and producing exceptionally smooth and uniform surfaces. Credit: Amazon

FIG. 18. Master Airbrush Cool Runner II Dual Fan Air Compressor Airbrushing System Kit with 3 Professional Airbrushes, Credit: Amazon.

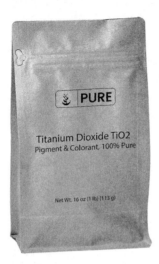

FIG. 19. Titanium Dioxide TiO2 (1 lb.), Eco-Friendly Packaging, Naturally Occurring Mineral, pH Neutral. Credit: Amazon.

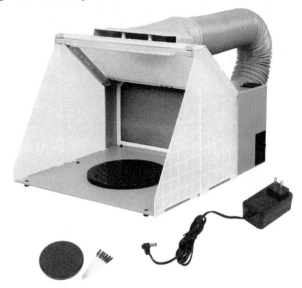

FIG. 20. TUFFIOM Airbrush Spay Booth w/LED Lights Fan Filter & 6 ft Exhaust Hose. Credit: Amazon.

Another use of an airbrush is for painting the surface of a workpiece, either before lasering, or after. Applying a surface treatment prior to lasering is appropriate in a number of circumstances, because precoating, as in the case of the Norton Method, provides the laser with a surface that it can react to. For example, laser engraving on acrylic or glass, without some pretreatment, has virtually no imaging affect at all. The laser light goes right through the material. With the application of a dark, usually black, coating, the laser can react and form an image on acrylic.

After a workpiece has been imaged it can be quickly and uniformly painted with an airbrush. Some of the advantages are that there will be no brush marks; multiple thin coats can be applied, including coats of primer; smooth color transitions and shading can be produced; custom colors can be mixed; and it can be more economical than the spray-can method.

As another example, the laser cutter can make a stencil, which can be used with an airbrush to quickly apply a design or marking on any number of flat or curved items. The stencil, made of paper, cardboard, or oil board, can be retained for repeated use.

Like any process that is airborne, airbrushing presents some health and safety concerns. First, the user should wear personal protection, including a respirator or mask, to avoid inhalation of fumes, and safety glasses. Appropriate clothing should also be considered. Second, the user needs to protect items in the immediate environment from being covered with unwanted paint spray. Both concerns can be addressed with the use of a spray booth (FIG. 20) that can both limit the range of spray and expel any fumes out of the immediate area.

Eye Safety

Any process using a laser presents a real safety concern. It should be obvious that the operator should not look directly at the laser when it is in use. Doing so can penetrate the pupil and focus directly on the retina. Permanent eye damage can occur quickly. The severity of eye damage is a function of the class of laser in use, and how it was viewed (direct, diffuse, reflected, scattered, etc. radiation). Even if the possibility of exposure is remote, adequate eye protection should always be worn.

Most laser engravers/cutters have an optional enclosure (FIG. 21) to minimize the operator's exposure to the intense light emitted by the laser. Even with the proper use of an enclosure, the operator should wear adequate eye protection whenever the laser is on.

FIG. 21. Ortur enclosure. Credit: Ortur.

Selection of eyewear is based on the wavelength of the laser and the recommended Optical Density (OD). The proper glasses filter the light, only allowing light of a certain wavelength to pass through.

The eyeglass frame (FIG. 22) should fit comfortably, even if it is worn over prescription glasses, and be of a wrap-around design to keep unwanted light from passing though from the sides.

FIG. 22. FreeMascot Professional OD 6+ 190nm-490nm Wavelength Violet / Blue Laser Safety Glasses for 405nm, 445nm, 450nm,473nm Laser (Frame Style 5). Credit: Amazon.

Fire Suppression

A laser beam outputs at an extremely high temperature, and in the course of engraving or cutting it can generate smoke, or ignite a workpiece, some of which are known to be flammable, into an open flame. The flame can set the machine on fire and quickly spread to the building that houses it, and endanger those inside.

The first rule in fire safety is to be vigilant, and never operate a laser system unattended. The area surrounding the laser engraver/cutter should be clean, free of debris, clutter, combustible materials, and volatile solvents. Cut-outs that fall through a table tray or honeycomb base should be swept up routinely, and not be allowed to build up. An air assist system should always be used when doing vector cutting.

The laser enclosure cabinet exhaust system should be examined routinely, and any build-up in the exhaust blower and duct system should be removed. Any obstructions in the air flow through the device need to be eliminated, and a safety checklist should be established and used before starting any operation.

Fire abatement equipment, such as a fire extinguisher (FIG. 23), is an essential piece of equipment, although a spray bottle with water may initially be sufficient to put out nascent flames.

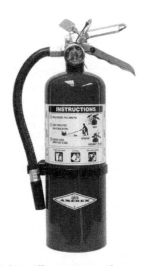

FIG. 23. Amerex B402, 5lb ABC Dry Chemical Class A B C Fire Extinguisher, with Wall Bracket. Credit: Amazon.

9. LightBurn Software

As you read in the introduction of this book, the software that enabled the desktop publishing revolution was Page-Maker, created by Paul Brainerd. The software that drives the laser engraving movement is LightBurn, created by Jason Dorie.

Jason, the owner of LightBurn Software and its lead developer, started programming in BASIC at age 12, and has been essentially self-taught since that time. His career has spanned more than 20 years, with extensive contributions in the video game industry, with more than 12 years working on the NBA2K game franchise. In 2016, following his work with video games, he joined Apple as a Senior Software Engineer in the Special Projects Group. His move to Silicon Valley necessitated selling his large CNC machine. He replaced it with a smaller laser cutter which came with RDWorks (https://rdworks.software.informer.com/), a free program for laser engraving and cutting. RDWorks has a number of shortcomings, and for Jason, the most significant of them was that his girlfriend, a graphic designer, hated it. Her love for, and familiarity with, Adobe products, was his motivation for creating LightBurn, which was originally intended to be only for Jason himself, and his girlfriend. Postings on social media soon showed that there was widespread interest in a more useable, professional-level software application. On January 1, 2018 LightBurn software was released for sale.

LightBurn is the software interface through which a user is able to control a laser engraver/cutter. It provides the means by which files can be imported from other sources, and directly composed, designed, and edited. A wide variety of popular vector graphic and image file formats* are supported with the use of powerful tools and options for creating, arranging and manipulating images, shapes, and complex layouts. The software, written natively for Windows, Mac OS, and Linux, is available for a free 30-day trial period at https://lightburnsoftware.com.

In order to run LightBurn the user must activate the free trial, or enter a purchased one-year license number. After properly connecting

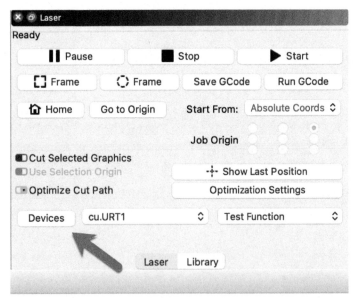

FIG. 1. The LightBurn software is intelligent enough to identify the laser engraver that it is controlling. It can be configured to control more than one laser engraver.

*Supported file formats include AI, BMP, DXF, GIF, JPG, PDF, PLT, PNG, and SVG.

the laser engraver via USB, LightBurn can automatically configure it by selecting the Devices button in the Laser window (FIG. 1).

Using the Find My Laser button in the Devices window, the software automatically locates the connected laser engraver device. The user inputs the size of the laser bed, the relative point of origin, and the home location at start-up. From here the user clicks on OK, and the connection is verified (FIG. 2).

FIG. 2. Clicking OK in the Devices window secures the connection between LightBurn and the connected laser engraver/cutter.

The LightBurn software is now in a ready state, with the connection confirmed in the Console window, and the Ready status displayed in the Laser window along with the user-supplied name of the laser engraver (FIG. 3).

The LightBurn Interface
LightBurn is an incredibly capable application that enables its user to access virtually all of the capabilities of a wide variety of laser engraver/cutters. An experienced computer user will find many of the

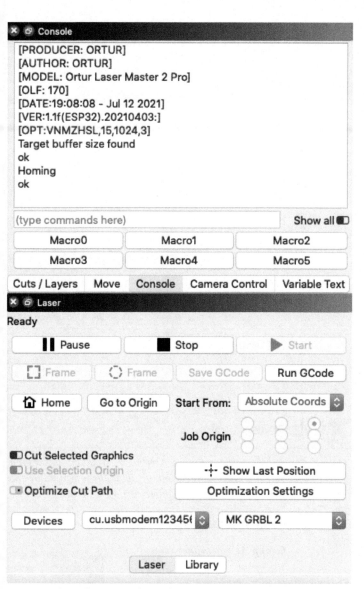

FIG. 3. The information displayed in the Console and Laser windows shows that the Ortur Laser Master 2 Pro is connected and ready.

panels, menus, buttons, and windows fairly self-evident, however the depth of the program will require most users to rely on the extensive documentation available at https://lightburnsoftware.github.io/NewDocs/index.html. A PDF version of the documentation can be found at https://lightburnsoftware.github.io/NewDocs/LightBurn-Docs.pdf.

The main window (FIG. 4) consists of icons along the top and left sides, the main composition window in the center, and nested windows on the right. Hovering the mouse over most elements will display a tooltip with their name, a short description, and their keyboard shortcut. A status bar along the bottom of the screen sometimes displays context-related information.

Each of the major interface sections is organized according to its related functions.

The Main Toolbar
The Main Toolbar is sectioned off by logical groups of functions, separated by dotted vertical lines.

Group One: *File related:* New, Open, Save, Import

Group Two: *Reverse action:* Undo, Redo

Group Three: *Clipboard:* Copy, Cut, Paste, Delete

Group Four: *Viewing:* Pan/Drag View, Zoom to Page, Zoom In, Zoom Out, Zoom to Frame Selection, Update the Background from the Camera

Group Five: Preview

Group Six: *Settings:* General Settings, Device Settings

Group Seven: Group, Ungroup

Group Eight: *Mirror:* Mirror Selection Vertically, Mirror Selection Horizontally, Mirror the current selection across a line

Group Nine: *Alignment left, right, center:* Align vertical and horizontal centers, Align selected objects along left edges, Align selected objects along their vertical centers, Align selected objects along right edges

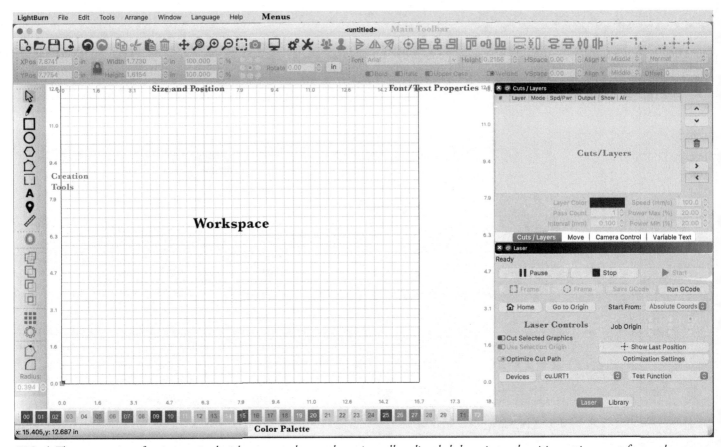

FIG. 4. *The program interface is organized with menus at the top, the main toolbar directly below, size and position settings next, font and text properties to its right; creation tools on the left, the job workspace in the center, and the Cuts/Layers and Laser windows on the right. The program interface may differ slightly depending on the operating system. All screen grabs shown in this book are taken from the Macintosh version of the software.*

Group Ten: *Alignment top, bottom:* Align selected objects along top edges, Align selected objects along their horizontal centers, Align selected objects along bottom edges

Group Eleven: *Equalize:* Make selected items same width, Make selected items same height

Group Twelve: *Distribute:* Distribute selected objects vertically on centers, Distribute selected objects vertically with even spacing between them, Distribute selected objects horizontally on centers, Distribute selected objects horizontally with even spacing between them

Group Thirteen: *Page position:* Move to upper left of page, Move to upper right of page, Move to lower left of page, Move to lower right of page, Move to center of page, Move to laser position

The Creation and Modifier Tools

Group A: Workspace tools:

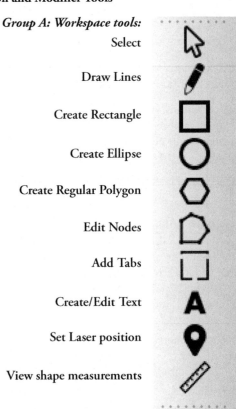

Select

Draw Lines

Create Rectangle

Create Ellipse

Create Regular Polygon

Edit Nodes

Add Tabs

Create/Edit Text

Set Laser position

View shape measurements

Group B: Offset

Group C: Wield all selected shapes together, Bool-
ean Union of two shapes,
Boolean Subtract, Boolean
Intersection of two shapes

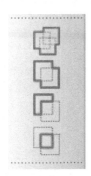

Group D: Create an Array of
selected objects, Create Grid
Array

Group E: Set shape start
point, Click corners to round
them

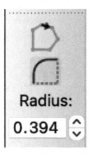

The Color Palette

The color palette is located at the bottom of the LightBurn window. The numbered colors in the palette are representative of operations that are assigned to shapes and other elements that compose the design in the workspace. The colors themselves have no meaning since the laser only generates a monochrome color. The choice of colors is arbitrary, although red is usually used to signify a cut layer.

Colors can be assigned prior to the creation of a shape or after. Once assigned, the colors are displayed in the Cuts/Layers window where their associated operations can be assigned. Each color represents a layer, independent of other operations that reside on their own layer. Each color can be specified for Output, Show (display), and Air (air assist).

The last two layers in the palette, T1 and T2, are reserved as Tool Layers. These layers have no affect on output, and do not control any aspect of the laser. These layers can be used for drawing non-printing guidelines that can be used for alignment or positioning, typing notes about material specs, masking image areas, and more.

The Cuts/Layers Window

Each color assigned to a layer has a contingent of settings that define

how it will be processed. First is the name, indicated by #, which defaults to the color palette number. The user can elect to change that value to a more descriptive name by double-clicking it, and entering text in the Name field in the Cut Settings Editor. The Cut Settings Editor provides access to many additional options. Name is followed by the Color, then the Mode, which can be Line, Fill, both, or Image. Next is the Speed and Power, which are critical settings for achieving optimum results. The next three options are ON/OFF settings for Output, Show, and Air.

The Numeric Edits Toolbar

Precise size measurement, position, and rotation can be specified in the Numeric Edits toolbar. Input can be in inches or mm, with each number entry box capable of computing calculations, as well as understanding various forms of notation, such as 7.7", 7mm, 7.7in, and 3*2". The 9-dot control array enables the user to select the point at which positioning and resizing occurs.

Fonts and Text Controls

Selection of the Create/Edit Text tool, or a text object in the workspace, will activate the Font and Text toolbar. From here the user can change the font, size, the letterspacing (Hspace), case (upper/lower), bold, italic, alignment, and data assignments.

The Laser Window

The Laser window shows the name of the connected laser and its status (disconnected, ready). The options it displays are dependent upon the particular laser selected and what functions it is capable of performing.

The Frame option may be one of the most used functions in LightBurn, since it moves the laser in a sweeping movement to indicate the area that the laser will be working within. Holding the shift key along with the Frame button will fire the laser at low power to show more accurately the outline of the area to be cut/engraved.*

The Workspace Area

The workspace is the area where the user creates their design, or imports elements from outside sources. The size of the workspace, 400mm x 400mm, represents the work area of the Ortur Laser Master 2 Pro, as input by the user during the initial set-up.

The user can zoom in or out using the plus or minus keys, or scrolling the mouse wheel while pointing to a particular element. With the use of the Pan and Zoom buttons on the main toolbar the user can quickly move to and magnify any element or area on the workspace.

*In order to activate the laser beam for the Frame function, the user must Enable laser fire button in the Device Settings for Test Function window located in Edit: Device Settings. After initiating the setting, LightBurn must be quit and then restarted. Upon restart the Move window will display a Power level setting, which should be set to a minimally low level, so that it is visible, but does not affect the material it is shining on. Pressing the Fire button will activate the laser beam. At this point the laser beam will be active when the shift key is held while clicking on the Frame button.

Elements that have been composed on the workspace can be selected by pointing at them with the mouse, and clicking. When a shape has been selected it appears with an animated pattern of dashed lines. Edit handles appear for moving, resizing, and rotating. Any changes made by the user are reflected in the Numeric Edits toolbar.

Elements can be deselected by tapping the Esc key or by clicking in any empty space. Two or more shapes can be selected by holding the left mouse button and dragging a rectangle around them from left to right. This creates a red rectangle; and the motion, which only selects items that are fully within the rectangle, is referred to as an *enclosing selection*. Conversely, dragging from right to left creates a green rectangle. This motion selects anything that it comes in contact with.

Selections can be modified in a variety of ways. For example, holding Shift while selecting will add the new selection to current selection. Holding Ctrl+ Shift will remove the new selection from the current one. Holding Ctrl alone will toggle the selection state of the new selection. Additional selection options are available in the Edit menu.

Project Procedure

Having read this far there is no doubt you have a pent-up need to produce something; anything, to show that your laser engraver works, and that you can control it. Here are the very basic steps to design and produce a simple project.

1. Open LightBurn.

2. Select the Create/Edit Text tool. Position the cursor in the middle of the workspace and type your first and last initials.

3. Select a typeface of your choice.

4. Set the type height to approximately 1".

5. Click the Select tool button, or click Esc.

6. Open the Cuts/Layers window. Here you will see that the initials you entered are on layer 00, drawn as lines, with a speed of 100 mm/sec, and a power of 20%. The line designation will produce the letters as outlines. These settings are defaults.

7. Select the Preview button on the top of the LightBurn window. The initials you typed will appear in the Preview window (FIG. 5). Click the Play button to see how the laser will form your initials on the surface of the material it will image. The black lines indicate the image that will be burned, and the red lines show the laser movements. The animation speed can be controlled with the Playback Speed setting, and the laser position simulation can be stepped forward or backward by moving the slider left or right. Notice that an estimate of the processing time appears in the lower right corner of the window. It is advisable to preview every job to avoid errors and to get an estimate of processing time.

8. Select the initials and try various fonts. When you have one that you like, change the Mode setting in Cuts/Layers to Fill. This will

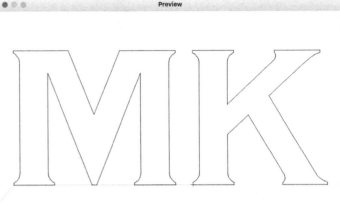

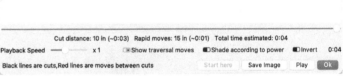

FIG. 5. The Preview function is an exceptional feature that presents an accurate animation of the laser movement, along with a depiction of the completed workpiece, and an estimate of the processing time.

produce solid text, with the letters filled in. Again, select the Preview button and view animation for the filled characters. Also, notice that the time has increased significantly.

9. Select the Create Regular Polygon tool. Hold the shift key and draw a polygon large enough to enclose the initials (FIG. 6). Select both the initials and the polygon and select the Align selected object along their vertical centers (FIG. 7).

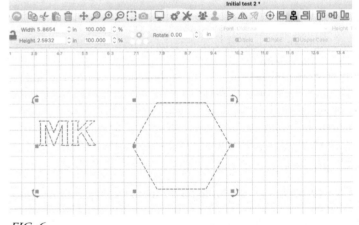

FIG. 6

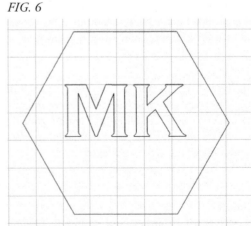

FIG. 7

10. Select the polygon and the Blue button in the color palette to add the shape on its own layer. Be sure that the Mode is "Line."

11. Select the initial and the polygon and click on the Offset Shapes tool. The Offset window will appear. Select Direction Outward, and Corner Style Round. You will see that the offset follows the shape of the characters producing an exact outline. Set the offset value to .25". Click OK (FIG. 8).

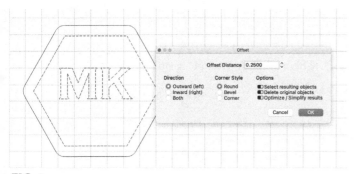

FIG. 8

12. Select the outline that you just created and click on the Red button in the color palette. Remember that red is used to indicate a cut path. There will now be three layers showing in the Cuts/Layers window. The job will look something like FIG. 9. Initials with default Cuts/Layers.

13. The speed and power settings are the most critical elements in successful laser engraving and cutting. They are very dependent on the machine in use and the material being used. Ortur provides a basic Material Library that lists suggested speed and power settings for a variety of substrates. Given the great variability in materials, the settings are only approximations. See the guide on page 20. Look for your material and enter the suggested settings for the engrave portion (black 00, blue 01) layers, and the cut portion (red 02) layer. To enter the values, double-click on each layer and enter new values in the resulting Cut Settings Editor.

14. Position the material to be processed on the laser bed. Hold the shift key while pressing the Frame button to see where the composed image will appear on the material. It may be necessary to repeat this process more than once to ensure that the material is used most efficiently.

15. Put on the laser safety glasses. The safety glasses MUST be worn whenever the laser is in use. Exposure to the laser beam can result in blindness or diminished sight! Do not under any circumstances fail to heed this warning. The laser is not a toy and must be treated with respect. The wrong combination of laser power and material can result in a fire. A fire extinguisher should be kept nearby, and the laser should be under constant observation whenever it is in use.

16. If all is in readiness, press the Start button. The laser should perform the steps that were observed in Preview window. If there is a malfunction, such as the laser stalling at a single X/Y position, or exhibiting a jittering or erratic motion, press Stop and Home. Remediate the problem and try again.

17. When complete, your job should look something like this (FIG. 10):

Optimization

As is true in any commercial operation, Time is Money. The most efficient use of laser engraving or cutting work involves planning that will reduce the amount of time that the laser head needs to move in order to execute its instructions. The less movement, the faster the job will be completed. Implementing an optimization plan in LightBurn will make work more efficient.

In order to plan for the order of executing instructions the user selects the Optimization Settings button in the Laser window (FIG. Optimization Settings button). This opens the Cut Optimization Settings window (FIG. 11).

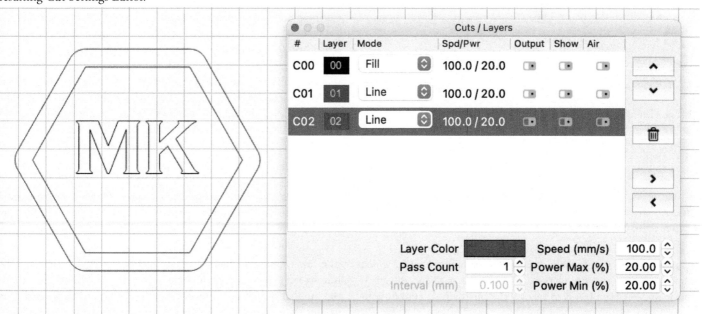

FIG. 9. Your completed job should look something like this. Note that the Cuts/Layers values will need to be changed.

be cut, to process them in the most efficient manner. Likewise, if a shape is composed of multiple cuts, selecting the *Cut inner shapes first* option will work from the inside/out so that the inner pieces are not missed, should the outer piece be cut first, and fall to the laser bed.

The operator, with the right selection of options, can ensure that the progression of engraved elements and cut elements, are produced in the smartest way, given the specific job characteristics and the capabilities of the individual laser engraver/cutter. Proper planning can ensure that should a job be paused, for any reason, the part that has been completed can still be used, and that continuing the job from the stopping point, will be easier, since all of the components of the job have been properly and intelligently planned.

FIG. 10. *The job looks exactly like the preview shown in LightBurn. The user may decide that the filled initials could be darker, or lighter, and might redo the job to achieve that effect. The results should be noted so that the user can collect useful data for their Material Library, listing speed/power, and other settings.*

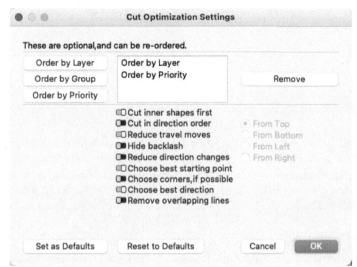

FIG. 12. *The Cut Optimization Settings window presents a number of options for programming the most efficient cutting order.*

FIG. 11. *Selecting the Optimization Settings button brings up the Cut Optimization Settings window.*

In normal operation, LightBurn cuts objects in the order in which they were created in the workspace, without regard for efficiency. This inefficiency can be overridden by the smart selection of options in the Cut Optimization window (FIG. 12). For example, the *Reduce travel moves* option recomputes the order in which objects will

Bitmap vs. Vector

A LightBurn job usually consists of one or two image elements: either a bitmap or a vector image. Simply put, a bitmap is an array of pixels arranged to form an image. For each pixel displayed on the computer screen, there is one dot printed by the output device. The number of pixels per inch defines the quality of the image, in terms of either the smoothness of the lines or the richness of detail. The more pixels per inch, the more image fidelity. Because each bitmap image is composed of a finite number of pixels, any enlargement of the image will result in image degradation, producing either stairstepping (jaggies) for line art, or pixelization (an exaggerated mosaic pattern) for tonal areas.

Bitmap images are also called *raster* images. A raster is a horizontal row of pixels or dots, and is a term that is derived from video display technology, i.e. television screens.

The key element in halftone reproduction is the line screen. The line screen is specified in lines per inch (lpi), and relates directly to the number of halftone dots per inch (dpi) that can be imaged. The greater the number of lines per inch, the more detail that a photographic image can express.

A continuous tone black-and-white photograph consists of a range of tones formed from reflected light onto a silver-halide coated paper. The printed reproduction of a photograph represents each tone as a pattern of dots, since a printing press, or a desktop laser or inkjet printer, using only black ink, can only represent a tone as the presence of patterned dots. When viewed at arms-length the dots are not noticeable and appear as tones.

The concept of line-screen ruling can be understood in relation to how a 300-dpi laser printer produces halftones. The printer can image 300 controllable "spots" or dots per inch within its bitmap landscape. But a spot is not a variable halftone dot; it is an immutable single-size unit. A halftone dot must be able to represent the total range of tones, from 3% to 95%, and a single spot, obviously, cannot do that. A 300-dpi laser printer, or a 300-dpi laser engraver, using a 100-lpi halftone screen yields a halftone matrix, or cell, that measures only 3 x 3 (300/100). A 3 x 3 matrix can only produce 10 levels of gray, unsuitable for quality tone reproduction. This accounts for the coarse quality of picture images produced by low-end laser engravers (FIG 13).

At 2,400 dpi, however, a high-end graphic arts imagesetter, platesetter, or other imaging device can produce a 16 x 16 matrix at a line screen of 150 lpi, yielding 256 levels of gray, which is more than adequate for producing a good halftone, i.e. quality photographic image.

A vector image is composed of line segments that are defined in mathematical terms, with trajectory coordinates. Each vector image is usually constructed of two or more objects, which, although combined to form new and more complex images, maintain their individual identities so that they can be modified independently. An important characteristic of vector graphics is that because they are mathematically based, they print at the full resolution of the output device. This means that vector-based line art prints smoothly, free of jagged edges. Vectors can be enlarged with no image degradation.

Bitmap images can be converted to vectors and attain the capability to scale upward without any loss of quality, as well as to smooth the contours of the image. Bitmap-to-vector conversion is accomplished in LightBurn using its built-in tracing feature.

The bitmap-to-vector conversion begins by importing the bitmap into LightBurn (FIG. 14). With the image selected the user then selects the Trace Image option in the Tools menu (FIG. 15). This results in the display of the Trace Image window showing the selected image with a traced outline in red. The accuracy of the trace can be controlled with the Cutoff and Threshold sliders. To increase the contrast between the trace outline and the image the user can select the Fade Image button. If the user clicks OK, both the original image and the traced outline will appear in the LightBurn work area. Selecting the Delete Image after tracing button will remove the original image when the Trace Image window is closed (FIG. 16).

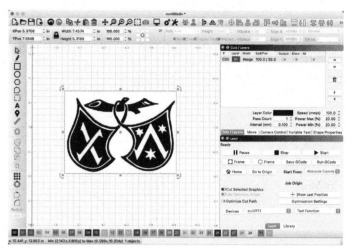

FIG. 14. This image was cleaned up in Adobe Photoshop prior to importing in LightBurn. LightBurn does not have the image editing capabilities to correct minor, or major image flaws.

FIG. 15. The Trace Image option is located in the Tools menu and results in the display of the Trace Image window.

A single 300 dpi spot

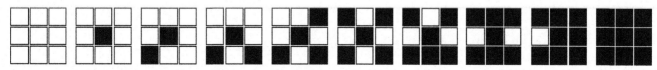

A 3 x 3 halftone matrix producing 10 levels of gray.

FIG. 13. The halftone effect is achieved by generating patterns out small mosaics of dot blocks called grains.

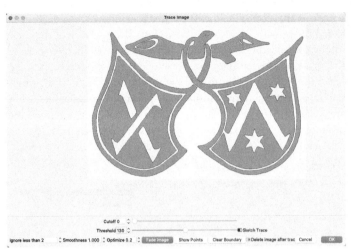

FIG. 16. The Trace Image window has controls to produce a traced outline retaining all of the details of the bitmap.

The traced image can be output as an outline (Line Mode), or a solid (Fill Mode), and retain its smooth shape regardless of its size (FIG. 17).

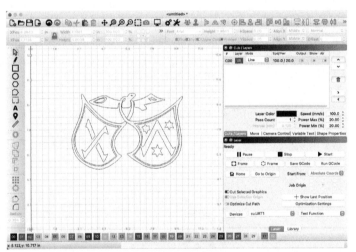

FIG. 17. The traced image ready for output.

Cutting and Engraving

The power and speed assigned to the laser determines if it will mark, engrave, or cut the material below it. When the laser marks the material it only penetrates enough of the surface to leave a discernable image. Engraving penetrates deeper into the top of the material to leave an image that is both visible and significantly below the surface. An engraved image can be felt by rubbing a finger over the surface and detecting that the image has been cut into the material.

Vector Engraving

The engraving process is differentiated into two forms: *Vector Engraving* and *Image Engraving*. Vector engraving deals with shapes and fonts that are formed from mathematical descriptors that drive the laser back and forth across the work surface. The laser turns on and off to form outlines and to fill shapes.

The actual laser movement can be previewed directly in LightBurn, to show how the laser will move, and what the result of that move-

ment will be. The letter L, shown in FIG. 18, is composed of a set of instructions that specify the coordinates that the laser will move to in order to form its shape. The laser moves back and forth, completing each raster sweep before advancing to the next line. The preview of that movement can be seen in the Preview window, with the red color showing the traversal moves of the laser that do not form an image (FIG. 19).

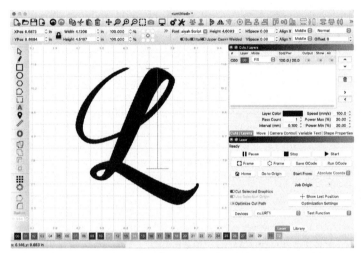

FIG. 18. Primitive shapes, such as rectangles and circles, as well as text, are native vector image formats.

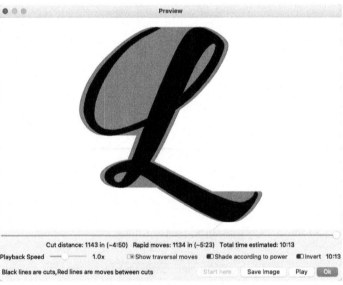

FIG. 19. The movement of the laser, as well as an estimate of its processing time, can be seen in the Preview window. The laser movement can be seen as an animation, by pressing the Play button, detailing exactly how it will form the workspace image.

The user can see the individual raster lines that form the vector engraving by enlarging the preview (FIG. 20). This view clearly shows that each vector image is formed by the raster movement of the laser. The number of lines per inch, that is, the closer the lines are to each other, the more detail in the engraving. The distance between the lines is set in the Interval setting in the Cuts/Layers window. The interval controls how much heat is deposited on the material, and subsequently the quality of the image produced.

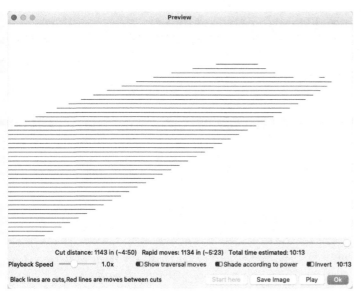

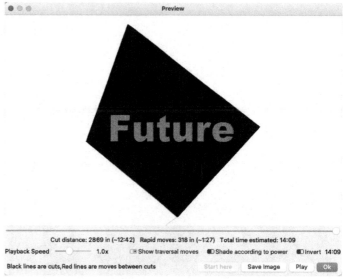

FIG. 20. The proximity of the raster lines determines the level of detail in the engraving. The raster lines are formed in alternate directions, moving from right to left, then left to right. This style of writing, approximating the pattern that an ox moves while plowing, is referred to as boustrophedon, from the Greek.

FIG. 21. At the end of each line movement the laser can momentarily pause and cause overburn.

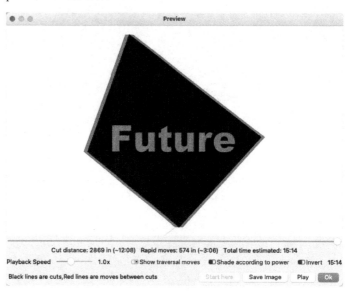

FIG. 22. The Overscan setting allows the laser sufficient time to attain the proper speed for completing each raster image scan.

The interval setting is also referred to the dpi, or dots per inch. DPI is a reference that should be familiar to anyone who has owned a computer printer, since it is the key determinant in assessing output quality. The higher the dpi, the higher the quality of image. This translates to characters with smoother edges and photographs with a greater range of tones.

The time required to produce filled images can be reduced by using the crosshatch option in the Cut Settings editor. This fills an image by producing lines in two directions, and alternately at an angle.

It is the function of the laser to transfer a precise amount of heat onto the workpiece to form an image or execute a cut. As the laser head moves across each raster line it needs to slow at the end of the line, reverse direction, advance to the next line, increase speed, then continue. During this process there is a momentary instant wherein it is still firing, and can express more heat at the edges, which can cause burns. This phenomenon is called *overburn,* and it is sometimes visible and objectionable. Overburn can be eliminated by using the Overscanning setting in the Cut Settings Editor. This setting provides a way to set the laser to continue past the end point of the raster line so that it attains the proper speed when it next fires (FIG. 21, FIG. 22). It is advisable to always use overscanning for both vector and image engraving.

Vector engraving is a function of how fast the laser moves across the workpiece, and what the power of the laser is set to. If the laser moves slowly, it will require less power to produce an acceptable image. If the laser moves quickly, it will require more power to produce a suitable image. Arriving at the right mix of speed and power is the key to successful laser engraving.

Image Engraving

Image engraving relates to the reproduction of photographs composed of bitmaps (FIG. 23). LightBurn automatically recognizes when a bitmap is imported, creating a layer of the mode type "Image." (FIG. 24) In order for LightBurn to process the image into a form that can be output on the laser engraver it must be converted into a pattern of dots. LightBurn provides several Image Modes that directly relate to patterns that have been proven to reflect screening characteristics that, to one degree or another, express tonal values. The Image Mode (Dither, Jarvis, Newsprint, etc.), along with other settings, determines how the laser will fire in the highlight, shadow, and midtone areas of the photograph. Remember that the laser is a binary device, turning on and off across each raster line to produce shading. The exception to this is the use of the grayscale image mode, which adjusts the power of the laser as it moves across a raster line. The grayscale image mode, is, therefore likely to produce the best results if all of the settings have been properly adjusted, and the workpiece has been tested with the particular settings.

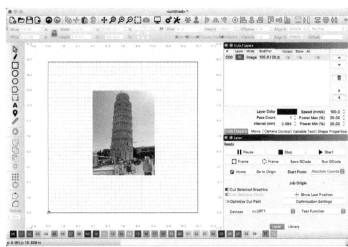

FIG. 24. *This high resolution color photo was converted to black-and-white and assigned the mode of Image as it was imported.*

FIG. 23. *The process of representing views of reality, and creating them in semi-permanent forms through the art of engraving, dates back to the fifteenth century. Using arrangements of dots, lines, and intricate patterns, engravers such as Marcantonio Raimondi (c. 1470-1534) was able to produce copies of paintings to make them more readily available to the public. He copied paintings by engraving patterns that simulated the content and tonal details, as shown here in Poetry Personified as a Winged Woman, ca 1515. Similarly today, the various screen patterns and LightBurn settings work to translate the tones and shades in a photograph into an image engraving. The inset in the lower right shows a set of steel engraving tools which are the modern equivalent of those used since the earliest days of metal plate engraving. Credit: E C Lyons Intaglio Set B (6 Tools) Etching Burnisher Twisted Scriber Scraper Elliptic Tint Burin, $96.* https://www.etsy.com/sg-en/listing/806313111/e-c-lyons-intaglio-set-b-6-tools-etching

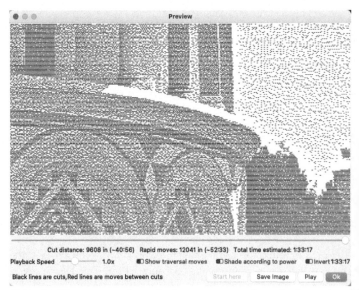

FIG. 25. *This preview shows the Jarvis image mode applied at a dpi of 300.*

The critical factor in image engraving, as in vector engraving, is the interval setting. The lower the interval setting, the more image elements that the laser will fire onto the workpiece. The higher the interval value, the more space between raster lines, the lower the quality of the image, since there is less visual content to view (FIG. 25).

The greater the dpi, the more detail that will be discernable in the image. The dpi is limited by the size of the circular laser beam in the engraving machine, which usually computes to about 300 dpi. The circular nature of the beam allows for some overlap, meaning that the dpi can be set higher, although doing so is a matter of trial and error. Running more than one pass can also increase the image contrast making it appear more realistic.

In selecting a photo, the user should pick one that has a wide tonal range, from shadows to highlights, with a significant amount of detail. Photographs that have big areas of a single tone are less likely to produce acceptable results. If the user is physically scanning the photo, do so in color and then convert to grayscale after. It is not necessary to scan the photo at a higher resolution than will be engraved.

Other image settings can improve the output quality. For example, the scan angle can help to minimize the inherent misshape if the device has an oval laser beam, which if not properly focused can actually appear as rectangular. Trial and error is the only way to determine the best setting.

Experimentation is an essential part of laser engraving, and what works for one user may not be optimal for another. It is important to keep good notes on all of the LightBurn settings and the characteristics of the workpiece.

Laser Photo Engraving Options

Although LightBurn has all of the settings necessary to process a photo for laser engraving, it is not the only solution. There are several methods that can be used to accomplish that objective outside of LightBurn, and with similar or better results. Using any one of them can still allow LightBurn to post-process such files, and send them on to the laser by using LightBurn's Pass-Through setting (FIG. 26), found in the Cut Settings Editor. Pass-Through, as the name implies, allows a file to ignore the Image Settings in the Cut Settings Editor, and instead retain those that have been applied in a pre-processing step.

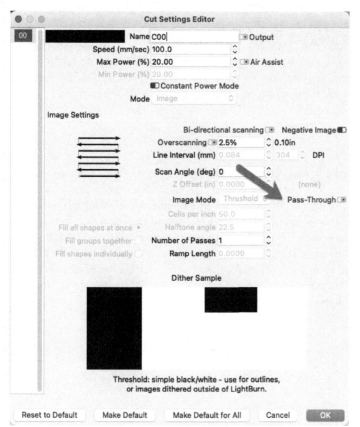

FIG. 26. Turning the Pass-Through setting on allows imported image files, processed in other software, to pass through LightBurn directly to output without being influenced by local settings.

Adobe Photoshop

Generally acknowledged as the premiere image editing application, Adobe Photoshop maintains all of the necessary settings to produce screened output with a wide variety of appearance options. Experienced Photoshop users can produce exceptional results, taking advantage of the professional tools at their disposal. Those less-skilled, or more time-conscious, can still utilize the processing power of Photoshop by using commercially available sets of plug-ins, that have been pre-programmed with a series of Actions (FIG. 27) that automatically apply steps that automate complex procedures. Running an action on a photograph produces predictable results quickly, reliably, and virtually effortlessly.

Photo Editing Service

For those users who lack both Photoshop and photo editing skills there is a Photo Editing Service for Laser Engraving available on-line.

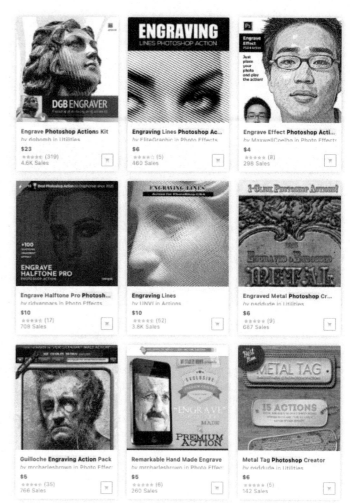

FIG. 27. Photoshop Actions are available for a wide mix of purposes, including, as in this case, for applying an engraved appearance suitable for laser engraving. A variety of free actions can be viewed at https://fixthephoto.com/free-photoshop-actions.

For a small fee, users can send their .bmp, .tiff, .png, or .jpg file to be processed and optimized for use on a specific engraving material, such as acrylic, wood, white tile, glass, or other substrate. Contact https://www.laserillusionstech.com.

GIMP

Users who want to process their own photographs for laser engraving at little to no cost can download a free copy of GIMP (GNU Image Manipulation Program)(FIG. 28), which is an open source image editor available for GNU/Linus, macOS, Windows, and other operating systems (https://www.gimp.org). GIMP has sophisticated capabilities that rival competitive programs. There are many YouTube videos detailing how to get started, and the GIMP website maintains several tutorials.

Specialized Software

Several software products have been developed that specifically address the problem of converting digital photographs into files in the best possible format for laser engraving. They include:

PhotoGraV (Windows only, $395) is a high-end software product mainly for professional laser engraving businesses. It provides its own

FIG. 28. *The GIMP program provides many useful photo editing features that can be used to prepare photos for laser engraving.*

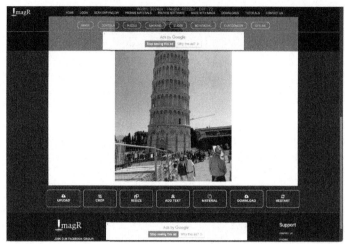

FIG. 29. *Among ImagR's advanced features are adjustments for brightness, contrast, and sharpening, as well as a preview of the file shown on a selected material.*

interactive environment for preparing and previewing photos as they will appear on the actual engraved material surface. The program specifically addresses the hit-or-miss problem of producing a workable file that is optimized for a specific engraving project. The main objective of the software is to output a file that will produce the best result on a targeted surface. PhotoGraV simulates a wide variety of engraving surfaces, such as cherry and walnut wood, brushed gold, and many more. A video describing how the software works can be seen at *https://www.photograv.com/wp-content/uploads/2019/02/Intro_to_PhotoGrav.mp4*

ImagR (basic functions free on-line; premium functions on- and off-line by subscription). ImagR is an on-line service that processes a photograph for output on a laser engraver by using just six steps. First, the user uploads their image into the editor, where it appears on-screen (FIG. 29), ready for step two, which is cropping. Step three is resizing the image to fit its intended output size. Step four is to specify the material (wood, acrylic, leather, etc.) onto which the image will be engraved. Finally, step six is to download the processed file as either a .bmp, .png, .jpg, or .svg.

10. The G-Code Programming Language

G-Code, also called RS-274, is a programming language that directs the operations of Computer Numerical Control (CNC) machines. CNC machines include 3D printers, laser cutters, lathes, milling and turning machines, laser engravers, and other precision motor-driven devices. In the case of a laser engraver, the code set consists of numerical instructions that direct the laser head to move along a specified path, at a prescribed speed and power, turning the laser on and off to correspond to a graphic design.

The earliest work on a numerical control programming language was begun by John T. Parsons of Michigan, in the 1940's. Parsons replaced the manually controlled cranks on wood and metal fabrication machines with servomotors, to automate their operations. His work was later subcontracted to MIT which soon thereafter initiated the MIT Servomechanism Laboratory in the mid-1950's. The language they developed, which was first input on punched paper tape, has matured significantly, and been refined to the point where it is virtually invisible to most laser engraver users.

G-codes are aptly named since all of their alphanumeric instructions begin with the letter G, and are preparatory in nature, prescribing exact actions related to machine performance. The code consists primarily of Cartesian coordinates that direct the laser head to a defined location, and set it along a precise path. The code to rapidly move the laser head to a prescribed X/Y starting position, for example, is G00. Assuming that the laser head is located at position of X=0, Y=0, the G-Code to instruct the laser head to move to the coordinates 15, 24 would be: G00 X15Y24.

The feed rate or speed at which the laser head moves is defined by the G-code command G01, and indicated by the letter F, for "Feed." G01 refers to a linear movement or straight line, while the G-code G02 refers to a clockwise circular interpolation.

G-code units are either millimeter, indicated by the code G21, or inches, specified by the code G20. Completed operations usually return the laser head to the home position using the command G28 for Return Home.

Some knowledge of G-code can be useful since it is the programming language that LightBurn software generates to direct the a laser engraver. When a user presses the Start button in LightBurn the program transparently generates G-code that is sent directly to the laser engraver. LightBurn also provides for saving the G-code to disc or to a thumb drive using the Save GCode button, or Alt+Shift+L, so that it can be carried to a laser engraver that is off-line and accepts direct digital input. (FIG. 1) LightBurn does not use the full complement of G-code instructions since many are superfluous to laser cutting and engraving.

G-code can be previewed using one of several free on-line simulators, such as ncviewer.com (FIG. 2). A G-code file, either written manually, or generated by a program, such as LightBurn, can be input, and each line of the file can be processed and displayed on the browser screen.

G-code is quite verbose, and requires pages of instructions to produce relatively simple images (FIG. 3, 4).

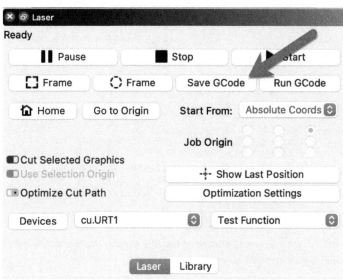

FIG. 1. LightBurn supports the output of G-code for the purpose of saving it to a media format that can be carried to an offline laser cutter or engraver.

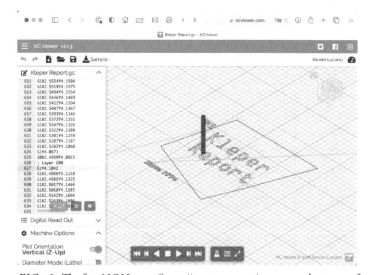

FIG. 2. The free NC Viewer (https://ncviewer.com) supports the input of a G-code file for previewing, step-by-step.

```
; LightBurn 1.1.03
; GRBL device profile, absolute coords
; Bounds: X23.65 Y134.74 to X361.8 Y289.24
G00 G17 G40 G20 G54
G90
M4
; Cut @ 100 mm/sec, 20% power
M8
G0 X4.3505Y15.4771
; Layer C00
G1
X4.365Y15.7623S200F236.22
G1 X4.3683Y15.8248
G1 X4.3718Y15.8813
G1 X4.3754Y15.9324
G1 X4.3794Y15.9787
G1 X4.3839Y16.0208
G1 X4.389Y16.0593
G1 X4.3948Y16.0948
G1 X4.4016Y16.128
G1 X4.4094Y16.1593
G1 X4.4183Y16.1896
G1 X4.4286Y16.2192
G1 X4.4403Y16.2489
G1 X4.4536Y16.2792

G1
X4.4686Y16.3108
G1
X4.4855Y16.3443
G1
X4.5043Y16.3802
G1
X4.5242Y16.4195
G1
X4.5429Y16.4607
G1
X4.5606Y16.5041
G1
X4.5773Y16.5502
G1
X4.593Y16.5993
G1
X4.6079Y16.6517
G1
X4.6221Y16.7079
G1
X4.6356Y16.7682
G1
X4.6485Y16.8329
G1
X4.6608Y16.9025
G1
X4.6727Y16.9773

G1
X4.6842Y17.0576
G1
X4.6955Y17.1438
G1
X4.7065Y17.2363
G1
X4.7173Y17.3355
G1
X4.7281Y17.4417
G1
X4.7301Y17.4654
G1
X4.7314Y17.4875
G1
X4.7319Y17.5076
G1 Y17.5251
G1
X4.7308Y17.5395
X4.7292Y17.5504
G1
X4.7269Y17.5574
G1
X4.724Y17.5598
G1
X4.7222Y17.5584
G1

X4.7204Y17.5546
G1
X4.7183Y17.5483
G1
X4.7162Y17.5398
G1
X4.7116Y17.5164
G1
X4.7068Y17.4855
G1
X4.7018Y17.448
G1
X4.6969Y17.405
G1
X4.6921Y17.3576
G1
X4.6876Y17.3068
G1
X4.6814Y17.2364
G1
X4.6741Y17.1674
G1
X4.6659Y17.1001
G1
X4.6567Y17.0344
G1
X4.6467Y16.9705
G1

X4.6357Y16.9085
G1
X4.6239Y16.8485
G1
X4.6113Y16.7907
G1
X4.5978Y16.7352
G1
X4.5836Y16.682
G1
X4.5686Y16.6313
G1
X4.5529Y16.5832
G1
X4.5365Y16.5378
G1
X4.5194Y16.4952
G1
X4.5017Y16.4556
G1
X4.4833Y16.419
G1
X4.4645Y16.3822
G1
X4.4472Y16.3458
G1
X4.4316Y16.3095
G1

X4.4174Y16.273
G1
X4.4047Y16.236
G1
X4.3935Y16.1984
G1
X4.3836Y16.1598
G1
X4.3751Y16.1199
G1
X4.3678Y16.0786
G1
X4.3617Y16.0355
G1
X4.3568Y15.9904
G1 X4.353Y15.943
G1
X4.3503Y15.8931
G1
X4.3486Y15.8403
G1
X4.3478Y15.7845
G1 Y15.7254
X4.3505Y15.4771
G0
X4.304Y16.9202
G1
```

FIG. 3. This is a small portion of the 174 pages of instructions, displayed in 10 point (shown here in a small sample in 8 point), required to output the alligator image shown below.

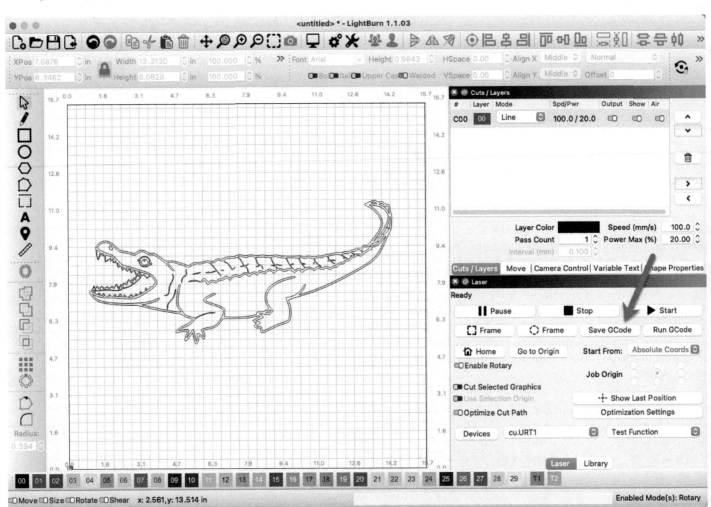

FIG 4. This simple line engraving requires a massive number of G-code instructions. LightBurn hides the complexity of G-code from the user.

11. Stencils

A stencil is a cut-out pattern, usually made of a thin sheet of paper, plastic, or wood, consisting of a design, letters, or both, that can be used as an impervious guide or template through which to apply ink, paint, or a layer of sandblasting, most commonly for the purpose of labeling or decorating objects.

Stencils provide a number of advantages for artists and craftspeople. A stencil can be used by almost anyone, regardless of artistic talent, to quickly and easily repeat a piece of artwork and/or text, and apply it on a variety of surfaces, using a variety of colorants.

A laser engraver can make stencils out of a variety of materials, limited only by the cutting depth of the laser for the given material. Care must be taken in the design of the stencil so that areas inside the counters of letters (enclosed white space) such as A, B, D, O, P, Q, R, a, b, d, e, g, o, p, q, are not cut out, obscuring the letters that they represent (FIG. 1). The same concern goes for designs that do not take into account how open spaces will retain their characteristic shapes.

Broadband
Normal Counter Spaces

Broadband
Missing Counter Spaces

Broadband
Stencil Counter Spaces

FIG. 1. A stencil must allow for any captive spaces, such as the counter spaces in certain letters, to be opened, in order to maintain their true shapes. A well-designed stencil can maintain those shapes while remaining true to the type design.

In order for characters that are laser cut into a workpiece to maintain their distinctive shapes, they must be created using stencil fonts. Stencil fonts are designed to allow for maintaining the counter spaces of all character glyphs.

The small links that stencil fonts use to connect the counters are known as *bridges* or *islands*. Users can modify a normal font, or given characters for a specific job, by using software like Adobe Illustrator, or the open-source vector program, Inkscape, to modify character paths. This enables a user to modify almost any font rather than be restricted to using so-called "stencil fonts."*

_____

*An excellent Instructables Workshop lesson entitled Laser Cut Stencil Letters, can be found at https://www.instructables.com/Laser-Cut-Stencil-Letters/.

There are also dozens of free stencil fonts available on-line from websites such as http://www.dafont.com, and http://www.1001freefonts.com. See the list of free and low-cost fonts in the Appendix.

Stencil fonts enable a laser engraver to cut characters into a design and have their design integrity preserved. The design of a stencil font ensures that the character shapes will be maintained as the surface of a workpiece is cut through (FIG. 2, see next page).

Making Your Own Stencils

There are a number of on-line tools that enable a user to make their own stencil fonts, or produce text in a stencil font.

Stencify. Stencilfy http://stencilfy.herokuapp.com by Tiffany Tseng, works by automatically slicing characters that have captive counter spaces, vertically. It provides three fonts to choose from, and allows the user to upload their own. Pressing the Stencify button produces a laser-cutter version that can be downloaded as a .svg file (FIG. 3).

FIG. 3. Stencify, a free on-line stencil maker that can convert any text into a stencil version.

Sun Catcher Studio Font Generator. Sun Catcher Studio Font Generator supports the production of typographic effects, including the generation of stencils (FIG. 4). The user simply types in their text, selects from a variety of stencil typefaces, sets the typographic parameters, and opts to save the file as a .png, .jpg, or .pdf. The service is free for personal use, however, users have the option of making a donation or purchasing a license for commercial use.

Font Meme. Font Meme (fontmeme.com) is a multi-purpose on-line font and typography resource, with a stencil font generator (FIG. 5).

FIG. 2. This scottie name tag was cut on the xTool M1. The name was cut using the free stencil font Running Start Basic, designed by Haley Wakamatsu of UkiyoMoji Fonts. The name tag is composed of two parts, the top with the stenciled lettering, and the bottom with a silver backing meant to highlight the letters (A). Glued together, the name tag is thicker and stronger (B). The red bow was cut using the blade cutter on the M1 (C). Combining multiple layers of thin materials enables laser cutters to produce workpieces that are thicker than any they could otherwise produce.

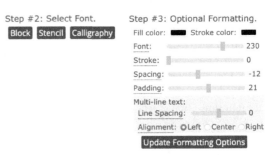

FIG. 4. In addition to generating stencils, the suncatcherstudio.com website has options to generate monograms, text in a circle, swash tails, and more.

The user enters their text, selects a font, size, effect, and color, and hits the Generate button, which saves the image as a .png file.

Create Text Graphics with Stencil Fonts

You can use the following tool to generate text graphics based on your selection of colors, text effects and sizes using stencil fonts in seconds. You can then save the image, or use the **EMBED** button to get image links.

Broadband ✕

SELECT A FONT

LINTSEC Lintsec ▾

ENTER FONT SIZE

88

SELECT AN EFFECT ▾

ABC None ▾

SELECT A COLOR

000000

GENERATE ✏

BROADBAND

FIG. 5. Font Meme uses its large collection of fonts to generate user-input text according to a specific typeface classification, such as Futuristic, Grunge, and, of course, Stencil.

Stencil Fonts. A simple Google search for "stencil font" will return hundreds of matches. There are both free and retail fonts available, covering a broad variety of styles, weights, and designs (FIG. 6).

FIG. 6. Here is a small sample of free and commercial font designs appropriate for laser-cutting stencils from 1001font.com. Fonts with a red dollar-sign button are free for personal use but must be licensed for commercial use.

Materials

Single- or low-use stencils can be laser-cut using paperstock or cardboard. If the stencil requires repeated use, the best material is Mylar, which is a polyester film that is both durable and flexible. It is available in a variety of thicknesses, and in transparent and semi-transparent forms, making it easy to align with the intended surface. Unfortunately, a laser cutter cannot cut mylar due to its transparency.

CAUTION: Vinyl, such as the type used in vinyl cutters that use sharp blades to cut designs that are lifted off of a paper backing and applied to the side of a car, a wall, or any number of things, should never be used in laser engravers due to the release of dangerous hydrogen chloride gas. The xTool M1, with its hybrid cutting blade, however, can easily cut vinyl materials.

Oil Board (FIG. 7). Oil board, with a thickness of .015" has been found to be a good surface for laser cutting stencils. Oil board is made from high quality paper board that has been treated with a mixture of oils that counteract ink or paint bleed-through. It is relatively inexpensive, and can be used flat, or around curved surfaces. Its main drawback is that it emits a strong odor. It is available from Jackson Marking Products Company, Inc., http://www.rubberstampmaterials.com.

FIG. 7. Oil board cuts easily and produces precision sharp-edged stencils.

12. Fabrication

Fabrication, as a process, usually applies to the manufacturing of a large number of material elements, or parts, that can be assembled to form a completed product. Within the context of a laser engraver/cutter, the fabrication process involves the use of a powerful, precision, focused, laser beam to cut an application-specific material into prescribed sizes and shapes. The resulting product may be complex, such as a precision multi-part functioning mechanism, or simple, such as the fabrication of a single three-dimensional replacement part.

Some of the concepts that are critical to the fabrication process are derived from the graphic arts industry. One, called Step and Repeat, is the creation of a pattern formed by repeating a particular graphic element again and again, at equal intervals, filling a prescribed space. Another, more specific to manufacturing fabrication, is the concept of Job Ganging. In printing it is critical to make the most efficient use of paper, i.e. reduce waste, and produce the highest quantity of printed output possible with the fewest number of sheets. To do so, it is common practice to arrange multiple jobs on a common sheet of paper, and then cut them apart.

In the realm of laser cutting the same concept is known as nesting. Nesting may apply to the process of positioning a single design or piece, multiple times, to provide the most efficient use of a work-piece, or to the process of positioning multiple designs or pieces to fit them together most efficiently and economically. The process is very worthwhile since it can result in reduced cutting time and better material usage (i.e. less waste). Nesting software can determine how to place elements in order to optimize common cutting edges, and arrange smaller parts compactly in available spaces.

An example of a free nesting program for laser cutting is Deepnest (https://deepnest.io) open source nesting software. The software can be downloaded and used at no cost. Available for Mac, Windows, and Linux, and supporting DXF, SVG, and Corel CDR, the program will process user files, endlessly trying various combinations of nesting based on a user-controlled configuration, until the user hits the Stop button (FIG. 1). The output can be saved as a DXF or SVG file ready to be sent to a laser cutter.

A browser-based version of nesting software, using the same nesting algorithm as Deepnest, is SVGnest (https://svgnest.com/). Light-Burn has incorporated SVGnest directly into its software, allowing the user to select the elements that need to best and most efficiently fit into a user-defined area. LightBurn has simplified the process into these steps:
- The user draws or imports the piece(s).
- The user duplicates the number of pieces needed. The user can quickly create an array of the pieces using the "Create an array of the selected objects" tool.
- The pieces are moved off of the work area.
- In the blank work area the user draws a box the size of the work-piece into which the elements will be fit.
- The user selects all of the elements: Edit>Select All.
- The user sends the selection to the SVGnest website using Arrange>Nest Selected.
- When the file is sent, the user sees this message in LightBurn: "The filename to import has been copied to the Clipboard. Click OK when nesting is complete."

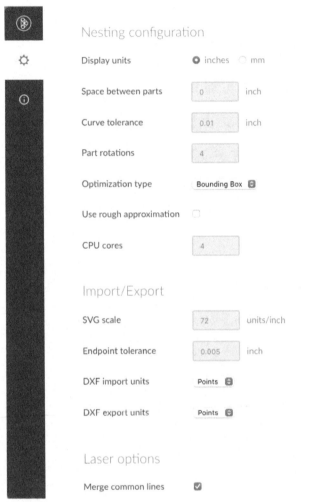

FIG. 1. The user can set a number of Deepnest parameters to control the nesting process.

- The SVGnest.com website opens automatically and awaits the upload of the LightBurn file.
- The user selects the Upload SVG button and selects the file, LightBurnNest.svg from the user's Download folder.
- After the job appears in the SVGnest workspace, the user selects the outline of the container, referred to as "bin," into which the elements will be nested.
- The user selects the Start Nest button. The nesting attempts will continue until the user stops the operation.
- After the nesting process has stopped, the user selects the Download SVG button.
- Returning to LightBurn, the user indicates that the file has returned to the Download folder and can be imported into the LightBurn work area.

- The nested pieces now appear in the LightBurn work area ready for output.

Multi-Layer Construction

One failing of most low-cost laser cutters is their limited capability to cut through anything more than thin materials. This, however, need not limit the thickness of workpieces if multiple layers are cut, and assembled one atop another. The options include:

Stacking: Layering and gluing two or more identical pieces to form a single thicker piece.

Layering: Layering and gluing two or more dissimilar pieces to form a single unit.

Shadowboxing: Adding spacers between layers to simulate a three-dimensional effect.

Mixed Media: Combining laser-cut wood, plastic, paper, etc. to create a single artistic piece.

For more advanced users there are auto stacking software applications that can generate slices of a 3D object, and output laser vector files for each slice. The laser-cut slices of such an operation can be assembled to represent the original 3D object. The process, although interesting, is time-consuming and beyond the scope of this book.

A Simple Real-World Example

As is often the case with games that have many pieces, a single piece may be lost or broken. In this example a critical part of a Rummikub game was missing; a foot from one of the racks was gone, rendering the rack, and therefore the game, unusable. Fortunately, one of the existing feet could be used as a template for fabricating a replacement (FIG. 2).

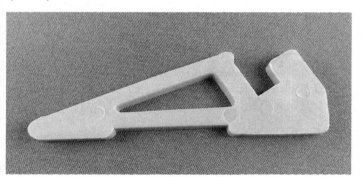

FIG. 2. Fortunately there were existing Rummikub feet, one of which could be used as a template.

The first step was to scan one of the remaining feet along with a measurement scale to ensure that the size remained constant from one image generation to the next (FIG. 3). The scan was edited in Adobe Photoshop to make the edges sharper and the contrast more pronounced (FIG. 4). It was then processed in Adobe Illustrator for a precise trace and then saved as an SVG file for use in LightBurn (FIG. 5). Alternately, the Photoshop file could have been saved as an SVG file and imported directly into LightBurn where it could have been traced.

FIG. 3. One of the remaining Rummikub feet was scanned on a flat bed scanner along with a measurement reference.

FIG. 4. The precise contours of the leg were processed in Adobe Photoshop.

FIG. 5. The Photoshop file was imported into Adobe Illustrator and traced. It was exported as an SVG file for LightBurn.

The limited cutting capability of the laser required that two layers be used (FIG. 6). The two pieces were carefully glued together and clamped (FIG. 7). After the glue dried, the edges and the surfaces were lightly sanded with 220 grit sandpaper. A primer coat, although potentially useful, was not applied. The finished foot restored the Rummikub set to its former glory (FIG. 8).

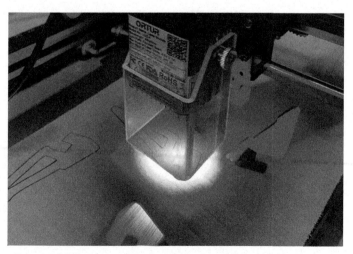

FIG. 6. The Ortur Laser Master 2 Pro cutting multiple Rummikub feet.

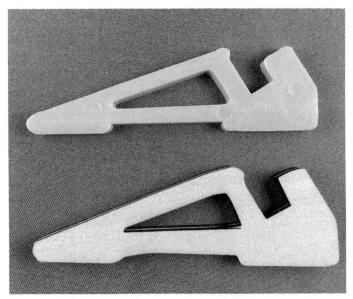

FIG. 7. *The original Rummikub foot above with the fabricated version, two layers thick, glued together.*

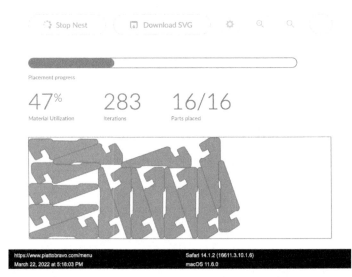

FIG. 9. *The SVGnest.com website has determined how best to arrange a quantity of Rummikub rack support feet.*

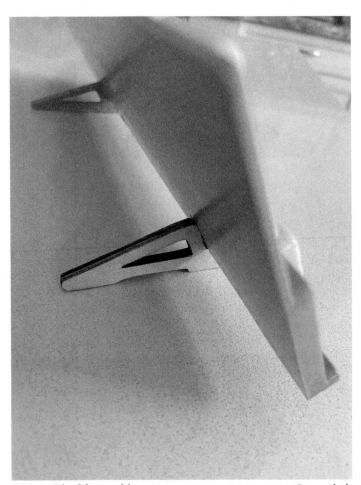

FIG. 8. *The fabricated leg, prior to painting, supporting a Rummikub rack.*

Were it necessary to produce many copies of the Rummikub rack support foot then the traced image could have been duplicated, and run through the SVGnest.com program (FIG. 9). The processed SVGnest result file can then be opened in LightBurn for output on the laser cutter (FIG. 10).

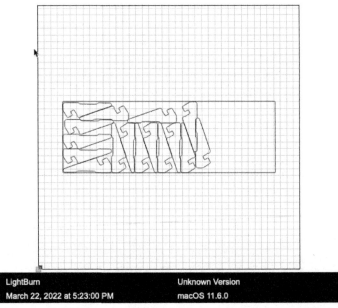

FIG. 10. *The SVGnest.com file result has been imported into the Light-Burn work area in preparation for output.*

The Paint Process

The paint process utilized PaintMaker, which is an on-line service that bridges the gap between the real and digital color worlds. It enables the user to produce accurate oil or acrylic paint mixtures that match colors selected from a digital image or numeric specification. A very useful introductory video can be viewed at http://sensuallogi-carchive.dk/paintmaker/video%20tutorials.html.

Determining proportions, shades, and color subtleties requires much patience, persistence, and ultimately a trained eye. It is difficult, and very subjective, even for experienced painters, at least until now.

PaintMaker is very accurate, however it is designed to use the exact paint colors from a particular set of a manufacturers' paint lines, such as Artists Oil from Winsor & Newton, or Heavy Body Acrylic from

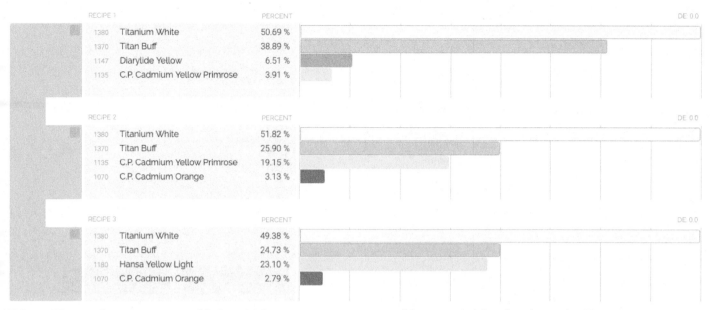

FIG. 11. Here are three recipes generated by PaintMaker to approximate an area of the Rummikub leg selected in its digital representation.

Liquitex. Fortunately, it can be used as a mixing guide for any paint line as long as it is a similar paint quality. About two dozen paint lines have been profiled so far, with more to come.

The PaintMaker process can begin by opening an image or by entering an RGB or HEX value. This may be an image that is to be used as a guide for painting, an image found on the Internet for inspiration, or an image captured specifically for grabbing a color sample for paint mixing. In the case of the Rummikub foot it was an image taken of an actual plastic piece (FIG. 11). Once opened the user simply places the cursor on the target color, clicks, and then selects the "plus" button to add it to the palette. By selecting a color in the palette and clicking

on "Calculate Recipes", the formulations can be displayed using the chosen measurement system (Percent, Parts, or Weight)(FIG. 12).

Even more amazingly, PaintMaker can calculate a variety of recipes using paint colors that the user may have at hand (http://colormixer.dk).

Paint recipes often require tweaking; making adjustments on-the-fly and using subjective judgements (FIG. 13). With time a user can get a reasonable paint match to the target color (FIG. 14).

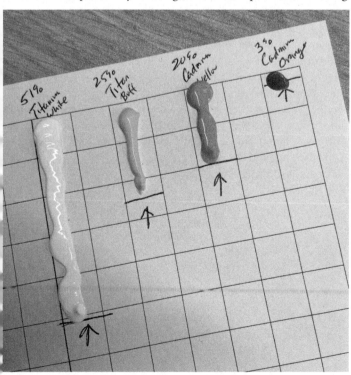

FIG. 12. Using acrylic paints that were on-hand, approximate amounts of each color were measured and mixed.

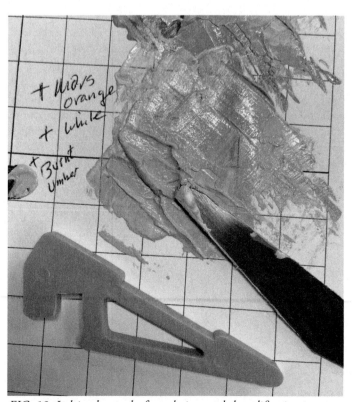

FIG. 13. Judging by eye the formulation needed modification.

FIG. 14. The wooden piece, in contrast to the plastic original, appears lighter. Further experimentation would likely get the color closer.

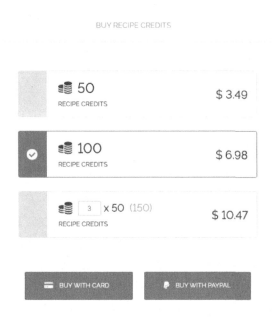

FIG. 15. The PaintMaker Recipe Credit system is quite inexpensive.

Each paint recipe calculation costs one credit, which is a means of payment. There is no time limit on when the credits must be used. Credits are very inexpensive, as can be seen by the chart in (FIG. 15).

The user may not have the entire complement of colors in a particular set, and can therefore narrow the formulation of a recipe by selecting only the colors that they do own. This, of course, can reduce the precision of the calculation, and may result in producing no acceptable formulation at all. When five or fewer colors are selected for the set, PaintMaker will produce a recipe regardless. In that way one can get a monochrome paint palette from a color image.

The idea for PaintMaker began in 2006, when Christain Skeel, a Danish painter became frustrated with mixing lighter colors during dark and overcast days of winter in Denmark. He contacted a number of paint manufacturers seeking a solution, but was told that developing such a system was impossible. He persisted on his own with no success until he contacted Anders Holm of the Niels Bohr Institute. Holm, working with algorithms developed by physicists Kubelka and Monk, found a way to calculate color mixing recipes. Producing an easy-to-use program that incorporated the algorithms moved forward with the help of Zsolt Miklós Kovács-Vajna at the University of Brescia in Italy. Each color in a base set is mixed with nine variations of white to create the initial image samples. The process of creating color samples for the system takes several months since they must be completely dry before scanning their surface. This drying process can take up to a year for oil paints, and several months for acrylics. The developers of PaintMaker should be applauded for their contribution to artists, fabricators, and everyone else working with colors around the world!

13. Rotary Laser Engraving

The typical open-frame laser engraver forms its images by moving the laser head in minute increments across its X and Y axes. This works quite well for engraving workpieces that are uniformly flat. There is, however, considerable interest in engraving images on objects that are cylindrical, and round, and may vary in diameter from one end to the other. In these instances, a rotary roller attachment is necessary.

Rotary roller attachments are available from a number of laser engraver manufacturers, and share some common characteristics. First, the laser engraver frame must have the capability to be lifted up to allow for the height both of the rotary roller attachment, and the object to be engraved. Second, a set of four variable-height risers, one for each corner of the frame, must be set securely in place to lift the frame. These risers should be modular in nature so that their height can be adjusted, as needed, in small increments. Third, the laser head must be mounted on a Z-axis height adjuster, so that it can be focused precisely above the highest point of the workpiece. Fourth, and finally, the motor that activates the roller assembly must be connected in place of the Y axis stepper motor.

Using the xTool M1 Rotary with the Creative Space Software
The xTool Rotary attachment comes completely assembled (FIG. 1). The xTool M1 is prepared for rotary use by removing its baseplate, and placing the rotary attachment in the center of the working area, with the motor facing the rear plate. Next the risers are placed under each corner, oriented horizontally or vertically depending on the diameter of the cylindrical object. The risers are placed horizontally for objects 3-20mm, and vertically for objects 20-70mm. It is important to ensure that the bottom corners of the M1 are firmly seated in the circular depressions of the risers, and that all of the risers are placed uniformly. The rotary is connected by inserting the white plastic connector end of the cable to the motor, and the aviation connector end to the port on the back of the M1.

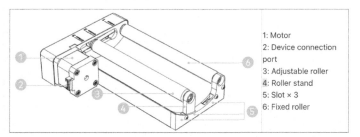

1: Motor
2: Device connection port
3: Adjustable roller
4: Roller stand
5: Slot × 3
6: Fixed roller

FIG. 1. *The xTool Rotary Attachment is very low profile and easily adjusted to accommodate a wide range of cylindrical objects. Credit: xTool*

The user selects the Laser Cylindrical mode in the Creative Space software (FIG. 2), measures the diameter of the cylindrical object, and adjusts the rotary gear as appropriate.

> For a diameter of 3-50mm, use gear 1.
> For a diameter of 45-60mm use gear 2.
> For a diameter of 60-70mm use gear 3.

The adjustable roller is moved, if necessary, by removing its screw, placing the roller in the target gear, and tightening it in place with the screw.

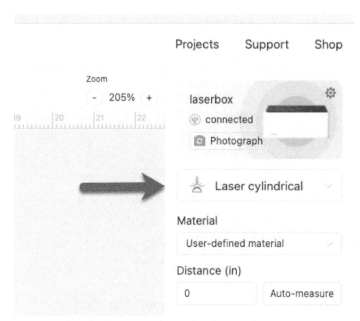

FIG. 2. *After the rotary attachment has been positioned, it is a simple matter to prepare the software by selecting the Laser Cylindrical mode.*

The user places the object to be engraved on the rotary attachment, and moves the rotary so that the highest point of the object is directly beneath the red light spot, which appears when the M1 lid is open, and serves to auto-measure materials. The M1 lid is then closed. When the camera is selected in the software, a yellow line appears in the workspace. The user drags the yellow line until it is at the highest point on the object, and then selects Auto-measure, in order to focus the laser. The user then imports a project file, or uses in-program graphics for processing. The image is sized, and placed closely to the right of the yellow line. Finally, the user sets the material, speed, power, and pass, and clicks Send. The Start button is pressed on the M1 and the process begins.

Using the xTool D1 Rotary with the Laserbox Software
The xTool D1 Rotary is identical to xTool M1, with the exception of the connection cable. The D1 is elevated to accommodate the rotary with the use of a set of spacer tubes that screw into the D1 legs. The spacers are modular, and multiple units can be added to increase the height. The rotary is positioned in the center of the D1 work area, with the motor pointed to the back. One end of the connection cable is inserted in the port on the rotary; the other in a port on the D1 motherboard.

Using the procedure described for the xTool M1 in the previous section, the rotary rollers are set, and the cylindrical object is placed. The laser head is adjusted by using its dropdown ranging rod so that it is focused directly over the highest point of the cylindrical object. The red cross-shaped positioning light is moved to the starting point of the engraving. The engraving process is initiated after setting the necessary parameters in the Laserbox software (FIG. 3).

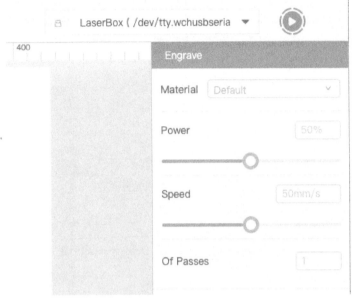

FIG. 3. *After positioning the image on the cylindrical object the user simply enters the engraving parameters in Laserbox.*

Using the Ortur Y Axis Rotary Roller with LightBurn

The Ortur Y Axis Rotary Roller (YRR) attachment is typical of a rotary device, with adjustable rollers and a synchronized stepper motor. It is an extra-cost accessory, in kit form, that allows the user to laser-engrave on cylindrical objects, such as drinking glasses, water tumblers, bottles, etc. (FIG. 4). The rotary attachment takes the place of the planar movement of the Y axis of the laser engraver frame. It does so by physically disconnecting the planar Y axis cable and plugging in the cable from the rotary device (FIG. 5). When installing, it is important to keep the laser engraver plugged in, but turned off, to get the benefit of the ground connection.

FIG. 4. *The Ortur Y Axis Rotary Roller is shipped as an easy-to-assemble kit. Adjustments can be done to accommodate a variety of cylindrically-shaped objects.*

The rotary attachment is free-standing, and must be positioned under the laser head so that it is correctly focused, and secured in a stationary position. In order to do that the entire laser frame must be lifted up, with risers positioned under each of the four corners. As the cylindrical object rotates, the distance between its upper-most surface and the laser must remain constant during the engraving operation.

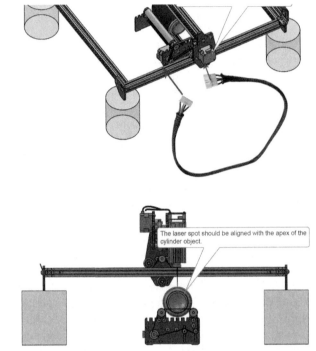

FIG. 5. *The laser engraver frame must be raised to accommodate the height of the rotary roller attachment and the target object. The user can improvise with various risers, such as soup cans, or use third-party risers such as those from King Gubby Designs (https://www.etsy.com/shop/KingGubbyDesigns). The laser must be focused on the upper-most surface of the cylindrical object. Credit: Ortur.net*

The process by which the cylindrical object will be engraved is dependent on its surface. The easiest and most direct object to be engraved is one that has a manufactured black coating, such as a powder-coated metal water bottle. In such a case the laser is burning off the coating in the image area, revealing the shiny metal beneath.

If using LightBurn, the process begins with the laser engraver on. The user selects Preferences>Settings from the LightBurn menu and clicks on "Show rotary enable on main window." The user clicks OK to lock in the settings (FIG. 6). Next, the user selects Machine Settings from the Edit menu to reveal the present machine settings for normal operation, exclusive of the rotary attachment. The user saves the regular operation settings using a logical name such as Normal Operation. To use the rotary attachment the user must turn off the Soft Limits and Homing Cycle buttons. These new settings are saved in their own file with a name identifying the settings as being associated with the rotary.

Next, the user selects Edit>Device Settings and turns off the Auto-home on startup setting and clicks OK.

Next, the user selects Edit>Settings and turns on the Show rotary enable on the main window and clicks OK.

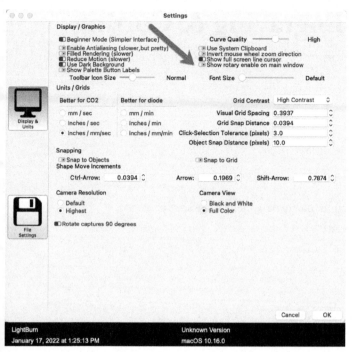

FIG. 6. The first step in using the Ortur Rotary attachment is to turn on this setting.

Next, the user selects Tools>Rotary Setup, verifies that the Rotary Type is set to Roller, and enables the rotary (FIG. 7). With the Rotary Axis radio button set to Y, the user enters the Roller Diameter by measuring one of the rollers. The diameter of the workpiece is entered in the Object Diameter field which also automatically fills in the Circumference field. The Circumference field value is used to create a custom template for engraving objects of a like size.

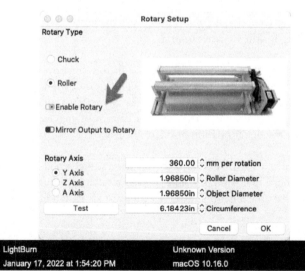

FIG. 7. Specifics about the rotary attachment and the cylindrical object are entered here.

In LightBurn's main window the user draws a rectangle in the 00 layer, with the height set to the value of the circumference. This dimension stretches all the way around the object, although the image itself may not extend that far. The width is set to the dimension of the area that will be engraved.

At this point the user should ensure that the template is positioned correctly in relation to the target object by covering the object with painter's tape and making a trial burn of a single line.

The content to be burned is imported, and/or created in the main window, and is inverted prior to processing.

The process used for other laser engravers may vary, but the fundamental steps are essentially the same.

Rotary Cup Leveling Tool

A typical rotary device does not account for the considerable variation in the realm of cylindrical objects. Tumblers and glasses, for example, are not always symmetrical. They are sometimes tapered, have bulging sides, or have narrowing or extended stems. Objects may be considerably longer than the rotary device, and may not balance evenly, or stay in place. The solution is a cup leveling tool, which is a free-standing device with adjustable wheels that can be raised or lowered to align the object and hold it in position. It is used in addition to the rotary roller assembly, and is usually purchased independent of the rotary unit.

In addition to the issue of size and shape, cylindrical objects are composed of a variety of materials, including glass, metal, and plastic. The interaction of the object with the rotary rollers can cause the object to slip or misalign, producing a sub-standard engraving. One solution is to wrap a strip of masking tape around both the top and bottom of the object to help it grip and move in sync with the laser. Another solution is to place rubber bands in the same positions. If the object is slipping due to insufficient weight, the user can wrap some weighted items in paper towels and stuff them in the cylinder.

The leveling tool should be sufficiently heavy to remain in the position in which it is placed, totally independent of the rotary roller assembly. The leveling tool's set of two ball-bearing wheels are adjusted in the Z-direction, to align the workpiece horizontally with the laser. The wheel assembly can also be adjusted 90-degrees so that only one wheel is in contact with the work object.

Several models of rotary cup levelers are available, and many have been designed using 3D printing (FIG. 8). The Premium Rotary Cup Leveler from Findlay3DPrinting, is available either as a complete ready-to-use device, or as a digital download for self-manufacturing. Both are available at the Findlay3DPrinting Etsy store. Also available with the cup leveler, or independently, is a rotary spacer that clips over the motor end of the rotary, and serves as a stop when engraving shorter items such as wine glasses and tumblers.

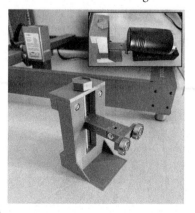

FIG. 8. The Findlay3DPrinting rotary cup leveler is a simple, yet effective, self-standing device. It provides a flexible support for holding odd-shaped cylindrical objects as they are engraved (see inset in upper right).

14. Materials for Laser Engraving & Cutting

There are many things to consider when selecting a material for processing with a laser engraver/cutter. First, and foremost, is the purpose for which the material will be used.

- Will it be used indoors or out, or both;
- Will it need to withstand moisture, cold, and heat;
- Will it be handled extensively or used primarily for display;
- Will it be used in contact with food;
- Will it need to remain rigid;
- Will it need to accept a pre- or post- treatment, such as paint or a clear coat spray;
- Will it present a hazard if it breaks, tears, cracks, or burns;
- Will it easily ignite;
- Will it score, perforate, or cut;
- Will it emit noxious fumes when processed;
- Will it exhibit sufficient strength for its intended purpose;
- Will it be cost-effective?

Material Thickness

The thickness of a material, particularly wood, will determine if it can be cut on a laser. For this reason, any project that requires cutting must take into account the maximum thickness of a given material that a laser engraver/cutter can handle. Here is a guide for comparing material thicknesses and their values in different measurement systems (FIG. 1).

Relative Material Thickness Measurements

Millimeters (mm)	Inches (in., ")	Nearest Fraction
3 mm	0.118"	1/8"
4 mm	0.157"	5/32"
5 mm	0.197"	3/16"
6 mm	0.236"	1/4"
8 mm	0.315"	5/16"
10 mm	0.394"	3/8"
15 mm	0.591"	9/16"
20 mm	0.787"	3/4"

FIG. 1. Relative material thickness measurement systems.

Wood

Wood is a readily available organic material that is among the easiest to process with a laser engraver/cutter. The suitability of a specific variety of wood is determined by its density; how uniform the density is; and its resin (sap) content. Trees typically give off resin as a way of protecting themselves against bugs and diseases. The resin content determines how dark the laser image will be: The more resinous the wood, the darker the color. The amount of resin can be affected by the season in which the wood was cut.

Soft woods, such as cedar and pine, tend to produce more resin than hardwoods, such as walnut and oak. The lower the density of the wood, the less laser energy required, and the faster it can be processed.

Resin content can be determined by doing a burn test either on a scrap piece of the wood, or by engraving a maker's mark or logo on the back of the workpiece. Another method, reserved for experienced woodworkers, is to compare pieces of the same wood species by eye, and judge the resin content…the darker the wood, the more resin. In general, lighter woods produce a greater contrast with the engraving, making it easier to read.

Wood suffers from its natural flaws and inconsistencies. These can result in unusable engravings, and in significant differences in the surface acceptance of the laser's heat. The presence of wood streaks can also significantly interrupt the dot pattern of engraved photographs or the line formation of vector images.

The vaporization that occurs when the laser strikes wood results in an edge burn that is unavoidable. It can be reduced with the use of an air assist attachment, and by selecting woods with a lower resin content.

Basswood. Basswood, known in Europe as Lime or Linden, grows mainly in the eastern parts of North America (FIG. 2). Its surface appears pale white to light brown, and has an even texture and a relatively straight grain. It is light-weight, odorless, and soft, which makes it particularly easy to work with both for engraving and cutting, since its surface is highly receptive to the intense heat of a laser. It finishes easily with stain, polish, or paint, and can easily and securely be fastened with glue, screws, or nails. Basswood is prone to warp when exposed to moisture. To overcome this deficiency, thin basswood is often converted into plywood which is more dimensionally stable.

Alder. Alder is a soft and resinous wood that produces a high-con-

FIG. 2. Basswood.

trast, dark burn when exposed to a laser (FIG. 3). Its surface is rather pale, although it may appear with knots on its surface which will likely detract from the engraving, or make it totally unsuitable.

FIG. 3. Alder. Credit: Stephen Ondich, CC BY-SA 4.0 <https://creativecommons.org/licenses/by-sa/4.0>, via Wikimedia Commons

Balsa. Balsa, primarily grown in South American rain-forests, is lightweight and smooth, which makes it easy to engrave, cut, and finish (FIG 4). The wood is particularly soft, and highly susceptible to dents and nicks.

FIG. 4. Balsa. Credit: Joseph Francis, CC BY 2.0 <https://creativecommons.org/licenses/by/2.0>, via Wikimedia Commons

Cherry. Cherry, as its name implies, has a light pink color when cut, and darkens over time to a dark brown appearance. Wood from the cherry tree, primarily grown in the Eastern United States, tends to have straight grains and a shiny texture. It is considered quite durable, and is frequently used in cabinet and furniture making. Its

smooth surface and low resin content make it a good candidate for laser processing.

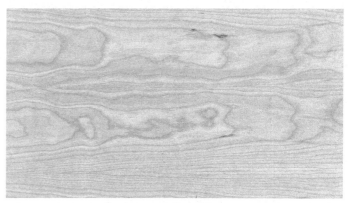

FIG. 5. Cherry. Credit: https://smokeyhilldesigns.com

Pacific Coast Maple. PC maple is particularly suited for laser photo-engraving due to its naturally light color that usually burns dark with little streaking (FIG. 6). However, caution should be used since its resin content is inconsistent, and maintaining quality control between pieces is difficult.

FIG. 6. Pacific Coast Maple. Credit: https://smokeyhilldesigns.com

Medium-Density Fibreboard (MDF). MDF, generically referred to as fibre board, is a man-made tan or darker brown product introduced in the 1980's, composed of hard- and soft- wood surplus fibres, i.e. sawdust and shavings, that are mixed with a wax and resin binder (FIG. 7). The mixture is formed into flat panels with the use of extreme temperature and pressure. It is often used in place of plywood since it is generally denser, and used in place of particle board since it is stronger. In addition, since it is manufactured, it has no knots nor grain, and is not prone to warping. There are three varieties of MDF, differentiated usually by labelling: ULDF, is ultralight MDF; green label is moisture-resistant; and red or blue label is fire retardant.

One of the downsides of MDF is its reaction to water, which can cause it to swell. This can be avoided by using the green label MDF variety. Another concern is its propensity to create an excessive amount of dust when cut, that can permeate the air and require remediation.

Cutting and sanding MDF may release resin binder fumes, which contain urea-formaldehyde, a known human carcinogen. Fire is a concern as well, as is the potential for charring during cutting. The fumes and smoke can also cause irritation to the eyes and lungs. All necessary health precautions should be observed, including the use of a respirator, and working in a properly ventilated environment.

FIG. 7. Medium-Density Fibreboard (MDF). Credit: https://smokey-hilldesigns.com.

Plywood. Plywood is a manufactured product composed of layers of thin wood veneer, rotated perpendicular to one another, and pressed together with an adhesive under high temperature and pressure. Its multi-layer composition makes it quite strong, and its surface tends to be light and smooth. Its glue content may produce excessive smoke, and cutting can result in fire. There are plywoods of various compositions, some specifically marketed for laser use, such as birch plywood.

Other softwoods suitable for laser processing include pine, cedar, fir, and redwood. Hardwoods include ash, birch, mahogany, oak, and walnut.

FIG. 8. Plywood.

Bamboo

Bamboo is classified as a "green" material since it grows quickly, up to mature height in 60 days, and is environmentally friendly (FIG. 9). Bamboo stalks, which are grass, are strong yet relatively light-weight, and can be processed into flat boards in a variety of thicknesses and shades. The material can be laser-engraved similar to other woods, producing a dark image. Small text sizes and design details should be avoided since the inherent pattern of the wood may interfere with their legibility.

FIG. 9. Bamboo. Bin im Garten, CC BY-SA 3.0 <https://creativecommons.org/licenses/by-sa/3.0>, via Wikimedia Commons

Cork

Cork is a natural material, has a relatively soft surface, and readily accepts the heat of a laser engraver (FIG. 10). Most cork is rather light in color and provides a good contrast with the black cast of the laser for engraving and marking. The porous nature of the material also makes it easy to cut. The downside is that cork can produce a significant amount of smoke, surface residue, and odor, which is best dealt with using an air assist attachment and an adequately ventilated environment.

Cork comes in a variety of grains, from fine to coarse. The finer the grain, the more detail that the cork will retain after the lasering process. Cork can also be painted to introduce color and contrast. Standard artist acrylics work well, and can be applied with a foam brush. The surfaces usually require two coats. The edges of the cork should be masked with painter's tape to contain the color. Painter's tape can also be used to restrict the surface areas that will be painted. Be sure that the surfaces are completely dry before engraving.

After lasering, the cork surface should be washed under cold running water using a soft brush, such as a toothbrush, adding a small amount of dish washing detergent to remove any surface soot. After cleaning, the cork should air dry. For added protection a thin spray of clear coat can be applied.

A popular laser engraved form of cork is the drink coaster. Round

FIG. 10. Cork. Buzzabuzza, CC BY-SA 3.0 <https://creativecommons.org/licenses/by-sa/3.0>, via Wikimedia Commons

or square cork coasters are readily available from laser engraving supply houses and other retail sources. Uncut cork, in roll form, can be secured from hobby supply stores, and cut to size using the laser itself, or by hand. Coasters can also be cut out of a portion of a roll during the engraving process by adding a cut layer that is the size of the coaster.

Plastic

Plastics used in laser engraving/cutting are of two types: thermosets and thermoplastics, each of which reacts differently to laser energy. A thermoset plastic can be engraved, producing a clear and high-contrast image. However, it cannot easily be cut since the plastic hardens immediately after exposure to a high-energy laser beam.

Thermoplastics have less complex polymer chains, and therefore fewer bonding connections. For this reason, they can be melted with a laser, allowing both laser engraving and cutting, although the engraving, under normal circumstances, can be virtually invisible.

There are dozens of different types of plastics available, and many can be used effectively in laser engraving and cutting. Caution should always be exercised since virtually all plastics release toxic gases to a greater or lesser degree. For this reason, users should work in a well-ventilated environment with an adequate filtration system, and wear personal protective equipment.

Acrylic (aka Plexiglass). Acrylic sheets, either clear or in translucent colors, are manufactured in two different forms: cast and extruded (FIG. 11). Cast acrylic which is very strong, is made by molding melted acrylic resins between two sheets of glass, and is preferred for lasering awards and trophies since the image that is formed appears frosted, and displays well with LED edge lighting. Extruded acrylic, made by melting acrylic resins and forcing the resultant liquid through rollers, is less expensive, and is softer. It has been found to be inappropriate for raster engraving since the image immediately melts back into the surface.

FIG. 11. Acrylic plastic. Black acrylic plastic is easily cut, as are other dark colors. Credit: https://smokeyhilldesigns.com

There are two common ways of imaging on acrylic. The first involves painting a black colorant on the surface and directing the laser at the acrylic beneath the paint. After lasering the paint is removed. The second is called "mirror reverse side engraving" wherein the image is reversed and engraved on the back of the surface.

Acrylic tends to become statically charged, attracting unsightly dust, lint and dirt from its ambient surroundings. This can be prevented with the use of a silicone lubricant spray which may need to be re-applied every few weeks. The surfaces should be cleaned beforehand with a microfiber cloth and a little mild household dishwashing detergent.

Vinyl. Craft vinyl sheets usually contain PVC, which emits dangerous chlorine gases when exposed to the heat of a laser. The gaseous discharges are very harmful to people, and corrosive to the surfaces of laser engraver/cutters. Craft vinyl must be avoided at all costs. PVC is known by Greenpeace as one of the most toxic substances polluting the planet.

Laser-Safe Craft Vinyl. PVC-free self-adhesive and heat-transfer vinyls are both laser safe, and are considered eco-friendly. They are recyclable, can be used without health or environmental risks, and provide for more opportunities for creative expression. The use of PVC-free vinyl is an easy way to add uniform color to a job simply by applying it to wood (FIG. 12). A popular source for these materials is Eco-Friendly Crafts, https://ecofriendlycrafts.com, e-mail: info@ecofriendlycrafts.com.

FIG. 12. PVC-free vinyl has been applied to basswood to produce laser cut pieces with color and a uniform smooth plastic coating.

It is possible that both PVC- and PVC-free vinyls may be used in the same environment. This might be the case when using an xTool M1, that uses both a laser and a blade-cutter imager. Vinyl materials, in such a case, would need to properly labelled and stored separately so that they are not improperly used.

Rubber

Thin rubber sheets have been used successfully to make rubber stamps by using the heat of the laser to remove non-image areas

(FIG. 13). Although known to be particularly odoriferous, some varieties, such as Low Odor Blue Laser Rubber, have been formulated to produce little or no odor when engraved.

Rubber sheets are usually sold with a thin plastic coating on one side, which must be removed prior to engraving. Engraving must occur on the side that was protected by the plastic, and processed on a vented cutting bed to avoid material melting. After engraving, the rubber should be washed with a mild detergent and water, rinsed, and towel-dried.

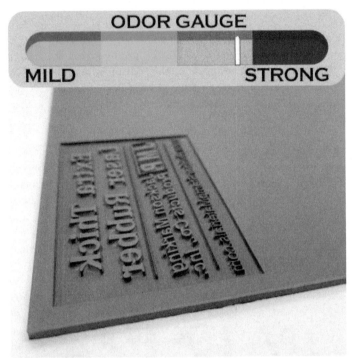

FIG. 13. Laser Rubber Low Odor Blue OG. Credit: http://rubber-stamp.com

Stone

Slate. Slate tile is a fine-grained rock that is commonly laser-engraved in the form of a coaster or sign (FIG. 14). The surface must be flat and smooth. Surface dust, which is commonly present, can produce blemishes and inconsistent imaging, and can be avoided by thoroughly wiping the surface with alcohol. The imaging process can be enhanced by applying a clear coat spray to the surface prior to engraving, and another after, to seal the image.

A variety of other stone surfaces, such as marble and granite, can be engraved successfully provided that their surface is polished and flat. Stone, obviously, is very hard, and will only accept a shallow engraving. Like slate, the image produced on stone is generally light or white, a result of the laser removing the base color from the stone. Color can be applied to increase the contrast of the engraving and its surface by paint-filling the image with a lacquer-based paint, and rubbing off any excess. Acrylic paints should not be used since they do not absorb into the stone surface.

Uneven stone surfaces can be engraved by supporting their weight on the laser bed with modeling clay, and exposing the flattest edge to the laser. Pebbles and various common stones can be engraved with

FIG. 14. Pieces of slate cut for use as coasters.

some experimentation.

Rocks & Pebbles. Rocks are naturally occurring aggregates of minerals that compose a large part of the earth's surface. They are readily available in the ground, from mining sites, and from commercially processed sources. Pebbles, generally found on beaches, lakes and ponds, are usually small, smooth, and round. They are found in a wide variety of colors and can be purchased in bulk at garden provisioners and craft stores.

The most suitable rocks and pebbles for laser engraving are excep-

FIG. 15. *These pebbles were coated with a thin layer of black tempra paint prior to engraving. After engraving the remaining paint was washed off. The surface can be lightly sanded and sealed with a clear spray or a coat of wax.*

tionally smooth and have a flat surface. Depending on the laser, the process will generally require more than one pass, and may, in fact, require many. The tremendous variety of rocks and pebbles, in terms of their surface variation, hardness, shape, grain, veins, and other characteristics, makes it impossible to provide general engraving instructions. However, experience has shown that a thin layer of black tempra paint, or a mask of blue painter's tape, can help to microfracture the surface. After engraving, the surface may benefit from a color-fill if the contrast is insufficient.

A variety of stone pebble mosaics, adhered to a flexible mesh backing, are sold in home improvement stores, and on-line shops (FIG. 16). The advantage of these pebbles is that they are flat on both sides, and are therefore, easier to engrave. These pebbles are easily removed from the backing by soaking the tiles in warm water to loosen the glue, and then scraping off the mesh, or by dousing the back with acetone, which will release the mesh more quickly (FIG. 17).

FIG. 17. An application of acetone quickly melts the glue that holds the pebbles to the mesh.

FIG. 16. Sheets of flat pebbles, held together on glued mesh, sold for use on floors and backsplashes, are readily available from flooring outlets.

Ceramic Tile
Ceramic tile will not respond to the heat of the laser without a pre-treatment. Covering the surface of the tile with white spray paint results in an exothermic reaction when struck by the laser, producing a permanent gray-to-black image. See the Pre/Post- Surface Preparation chapter on page 82.

Fabric
Most natural and synthetic fabrics can be laser-cut, including cotton, microfiber, nylon, linen, silk, and wool. Since the laser does not exert any pressure on the fabric there are no rough edges nor fraying, and multiple layers can be cut simultaneously. Fabrics need to be tight-fitting, since loose threads will cut poorly. The precision of the laser can produce cuts that would otherwise be difficult and time-consuming by hand. A few fabrics, such as fleece, denim and felt, can be laser-en-

graved as well. The recommended laser settings are low power and high speed, to avoid burning.

The majority of fabrics do not demonstrate any laser-related problems, however, some that contain plastic, as a coating or in a weave, or are made using PVC, are highly prone to catching fire, or producing fumes that can cause serious health damage to the users' lungs and the laser machine.

Paper
Paper is available in a wide variety of types, thicknesses, surfaces, colors, etc. Due to its thin caliper and light weight, paper cannot easily be engraved, but rather, it can easily be cut. Intricate decorative designs can be produced easily, without the need for an expensive die-cut pattern.

Cardboard
Chipboard, or cardboard, are terms used to describe particularly heavy paper, either layered or corrugated to increase its strength and durability (FIG. 18). It is inexpensive, recyclable, and useful for craft projects, such as prototype construction, architectural modeling, 3D sculptures, stencils, and signs. It is easily assembled with hot or cold glue, staples, or tape, and can be printed using conventional processes. The flat smooth surface accepts acrylic or tempra paint readily, although certain varieties can easily absorb paint into their surface.

FIG 18. Cardboard. Drina, CC BY-SA 4.0 <https://creativecommons.org/licenses/by-sa/4.0>, via Wikimedia Commons

Cardboard is made from wood chips, paper pulp, sawdust, wood shavings, and recycled paper, and is easily engraved and cut. Some forms of cardboard, such as corrugated, are particularly prone to catching fire. The material is not recommended for raster engraving. Vector cuts are best performed in multiple passes at low power.

Leaves

Leaves, green or dried, as well as other plant and tree foliage, such as palm fronds (specifically the leaf sheath), can be engraved or cut… but only with a degree of care (FIG. 19). The leaves need to be as flat as possible, and free of any evidence of insects, dirt, or extraneous surface growth (FIG. 20).

FIG. 19. This portion of flattened leaf sheath from a palm frond, measures 1.93mm. It can be easily engraved and cut.

FIG. 20. This image of an egret was easily cut out of a dried sea grape leaf.

In order to flatten the leaves, they can be pressed between sheets of paper, as in a book, or placed under flat weights to get the leaf surfaces as uniform as possible.

The structure of a leaf consists of parts of various thicknesses, which complicates the use of a laser. The thinnest, flattest, part are the venules, which form the main substance of a leaf. Running through the leaf are veins, which emanate from the midrib, which runs its length. Engraving on, or cutting through, most leaves, is easy; although determining the best speed/power to produce the best results can be a challenge. When cutting, it is best to use a setting that provides a clean cut on the venule. If the cut fails to pierce through the veins or midribs, an Xacto knife or other blade can complete the job (FIG. 21).

FIG. 21. This alligator image was engraved on, and cut from, a dried sea grape leaf. Parts that intersected the veins and midrib required snipping with an Xacto knife. Free clipart: http://www.clipartpanda.com/categories/alligator-clipart-black-and-white.

Canvas

Canvas is a woven fabric, commonly made from linen or cotton (FIG. 22). It is known for its durability, and is the usual support base for oil and acrylic painting. When stretched on a wooden frame it becomes an especially useful medium for the process of laser engraving photographs.

FIG. 22. Canvas. Cara from Boston, MA, US, CC BY 2.0 <https://creativecommons.org/licenses/by/2.0>, via Wikimedia Commons

Adhesive Materials

Several types of adhesive materials, all being very thin, can be cut and transferred for use as labels and appliques. Adhesive material can be laser cut, and either the positive cut or the negative background can be transferred, by first weeding out the unwanted areas, and then using a low-tact transfer tape to lift it, transfer it to its final location, and burnish it in place. Such materials must not be vinyl-based, which emit dangerous fumes.

Blue painter's tape has a number of uses in laser engraving, one of

FIG. 23. Blue Painters Tape. Imjustmatthew, CC BY-SA 3.0 <https://creativecommons.org/licenses/by-sa/3.0>, via Wikimedia Commons

which is to cover a given target material in the projected engraving area, and laser surface mark the tape to show how a given design will appear, without cutting through the tape. This is useful for previewing the location of a design prior to committing it to the actual engraving.

Blue painter's tape can also be used to vector-mask an area, essentially creating a stencil through which an engraved area can be painted.

Specialty materials, such as heat transfer sheets, can be laser-cut and then placed over an item of clothing in a heat transfer press.

Leather

Leather is an excellent candidate for both laser engraving and cutting, although it tends to smell when heated (FIG. 24). Its soft texture and generally slim thickness, rate it suitable for use of lower laser power and/or faster processing speed. In general, only light colored leathers should be engraved since they appear with greater contrast. Be advised that artificial leather is usually made from PVC which emits noxious gases which are poisonous and dangerous to humans and lasers!

FIG. 24. Leather.

Glass

Engraving glass can take patience and practice, especially if it is curved, like a drinking glass or bottle (FIG. 25). Curved glass tends to have hard and soft spots, whereas flat glass has a more consistent surface hardness. The laser heat can produce minute, sharp cuts, chips, and non-uniform engravings. Heat can be dissipated by uniformly wrapping a wet paper towel or newspaper around the glass prior to engraving. If the finished item will be used in contact with food and drink, care must be taken to ensure that no residual glass particles remain.

FIG. 25. Glass engraving on a piece of blue stained glass.

Metal

Metal is a difficult surface for a low-power laser to penetrate, or even mark (FIG. 26). There are procedures wherein a special spray coating can be applied to help the laser etch the surface. Coatings can also be applied to metal that a laser can burn off to reveal the metal surface. See the chapter on Pre/Post Surface Treatments, on page 82)

FIG 26. Metal card. MetalCreditCards, CC BY-SA 4.0 <https://creativecommons.org/licenses/by-sa/4.0>, via Wikimedia Commons

Food

For obvious sanitary reasons it is not advisable to laser-engrave food items. However, that has not stopped users from experimenting, and sometimes with success (FIG. 27).

FIG. 27. This chocolate bar has not suffered any apparent damage by undergoing a surface laser treatment. Credit: https://cartonus.com/how-to-laser-engraving-chocolate/.

Kerf

Kerf is a term originally used in woodworking to describe the thickness of wood removed by the teeth of a saw blade. Since the saw blade teeth are bent to the side, they remove more wood than the actual saw blade itself, thus preventing the saw from getting stuck.

The space that is formed when the laser passes through a material is also called the "kerf." Kerf can be a significant factor when joining pieces of a material together, such as assembling a box. The size of a kerf is dependent on the properties of the material, its thickness, the focal length of the lens, and even on the pressure of the air assist. In general, the softer the material, the larger the kerf. There is no absolute formula for computing the size of a kerf, although, in general, it can be estimated to be the width of the laser beam divided by two.

It is necessary to be aware of kerf since there is the general belief that "laser precision" ensures high accuracy. If high accuracy is the goal, then the cuts must be designed to allow for the amount of kerf; however, for most users, kerf will not be of any serious significance.

One area in which kerf is a positive characteristic is the design of "living hinges." Producing a pattern of close-cut lines in relatively thin wood material, not exceeding .25" allows the wood to bend easily. This feature can be incorporated in designs for things like boxes, without the need for hardware hinges (FIG. 28).

Material Safety

Rule number one when operating a laser engraver/cutter is safety. The purpose of a laser is to vaporize materials to form an image, or to partially or completely penetrate a material to crease, score,

WOODEN GIFT BOX

cartonus.com

FIG. 28. Many useful and novel gifts can be made from light-weight woods, such as this box with a living hinge. Photo courtesy of Cartonus, https://cartonus.com.

perforate, or cut it. As laser operations occur, the material's physical and chemical properties may significantly change, and in the process produce smoke, flames, fumes, gases, and/or sticky or liquid residue. The presence of any of these by-products can negatively affect the users' health, damage their machine, and pollute the environment.

What NOT to Cut / What to be Cautious of: Although a laser engraver/cutter is highly versatile, and can image and cut a wide variety of materials, some of them are potentially harmful and dangerous. It is known that any material that emits Chlorine or Hydrogen Chloride gas, such as PVC, presents a definite hazard to humans; and the potential flames they produce can destroy a machine, and the gas they emit can destroy the laser optics.

- Certain wood varieties that contain oil or excessive resins have the potential to catch fire, and should only be used with extreme caution.
- Plywood and composites contain glue and may not react well to the heat of the laser.
- Paper and card stock should be cut only as a single layer, to avoid fire.
- Cardboard is very prone to catching fire and should only be used with constant observation.
- Common packaging products, such as plastic milk bottles (high and low density polyethylene) identifiable with recycle codes 2 and 4, melt and become gooey, and should never be used.
- PolyPropylene foam, recycle code 5, melts and catches fire, and should not be used.
- Certain rubber stamp-making material can be safely used if they do not contain chlorine.
- Never engrave or cut polyvinyl chloride (PVC), acrylonitrile butadiene styrene (ABS), epoxy, high-density polyethylene (HDPE), polystyrene foam and polypropylene foam, and flame-retardant materials.
- The list of potentially hazardous materials is too long to list. Suffice it to say that extreme caution should be exercised when selecting materials to engrave and/or cut.

15. Pre/Post Surface Treatments

A unique characteristic of a diode laser is that it is a virtually inexhaustible source of surface-marking energy. There is no need for ink nor toner…the laser has an inherent capability to form a visible image on a wide variety of surfaces. The quality of the image, however, is dependent on the attributes of the surface receiving the laser exposure. Wood, for example, being organic, has great variations among wood types, with the possibility of significant inconsistencies even within the same wood type. Even wood that appears optically smooth, and has a uniform texture to the touch, may, on the surface have significant roughness (FIG. 1) and therefore produce an unacceptable engraving.

FIG. 1. This enlarged photo of a piece of commercially available basswood clearly shows the surface imperfections, loose fibers, and nubs that will interact with the laser to produce smoke, soot, and a lack of image definition. Note the grain lines that run from top to bottom.

Certain material surfaces, such as glass and clear acrylic, are impervious to laser light; letting it pass through with no effect. In order for an image to be formed, some substance must be applied to the glass or acrylic to stop the laser, absorb its energy, and form an image. This chapter presents methods to treat substrate surfaces so that they can maximize the power of the laser. Please note that the results of these methods may vary widely due to differences in processing time, laser power, mixing proportions, ingredient strength, operator error, environmental factors, and unforeseen circumstances. The methods have, by and large, been developed by users who have sought to make their laser engraving experiences better, and have generously shared what they have learned.

Pre-treating Wood for a Darker and More Detailed Engraving

Baking Soda and Water. The application of a mixture of baking soda (sodium bicarbonate), a white odorless powder, and water, has been found to darken and enhance the image of laser engraved wood.

Begin by lightly sanding the surface of the wood with a hand-held orbital sander with a fine grit sandpaper, to remove any surface imperfections, and to make the surface as smooth as possible.

Prepare a mixture of approximately two tablespoons of baking soda to 28 fluid ounces of warm water in a spray bottle. Shake the mixture to make sure that the baking soda is totally dissolved. Users have reported success with various other mixture proportions, such as two cups of water with two tablespoons of baking soda. Experimentation with this formulation can be worthwhile.

Spray the wood surface lightly with one or two passes, or apply with a foam brush. The thickness of the coat will depend on what you find to be the optimum. Let the surface dry completely.

The baking soda mixture has been shown to produce a darker image and reveal more detail, particularly for photos. The reaction of the baking soda with the heat of the laser also provides the benefit of requiring less power to produce the image than processing without the baking soda treatment.

A comparison of the same image produced with the baking soda treatment, and without, clearly shows that the baking soda produces a richer, darker, and more detailed image. Some users have observed slight yellowing on some wood surfaces using this solution (FIG. 2). To overcome this problem, it can be advantageous to add a small amount of white interior paint to the mixture.

Borax and Water. Borax, a white, odorless naturally-occurring powder, known as sodium borate, is significantly more alkaline than baking soda, with a pH of 9.5 compared to 8.0 for baking soda. This pH difference results in a different degree of surface darkening which some users find superior.

Borax is commonly available in a commercial product called 20 Mule Team Borax, and mixed in a proportion of one tablespoon to ten tablespoons of warm-to-hot water.

The use of the borax mixture, like that of the baking soda mixture, may leave an ash residue or surface soot. This can be cleaned using a damp Mr. Clean sponge.

FIG. 2. *The baking soda mixture can cause a yellow tinge on the wood surface, as shown on the right side of the wood. Notice too that the mixture has seeped into the left side although there was a barrier of blue painter's tape protecting the left side when the spray was applied.*

The borax mixture has a dramatic and intense affect when exposed to the heat of the laser (FIG. 3).

Steel Wool and Vinegar Stain. This mixture is well-known to woodworkers as an easy-to-make, inexpensive, stain (FIG. 4). This process has, in laser engraving circles, become known as the "Kenney Hack."

Place one 0000 fine steel wool pad in a glass Mason jar (although any glass jar with a lid will do), and cover it with distilled white vinegar. Partially cover the jar so that the reactive gas can be released, and no dust or debris can contaminate it. Wait two-to-three days for the steel wool to partially dissolve (FIG. 5). What remains of the steel wool will rise to the top. Stir the mixture completely, dissolving any remaining steel wool. Let the mixture sit for another day or two.

The vinegar removes the protective coating on the steel wool which causes it to rust. The exposed iron reacts with oxygen, releasing heat, producing an exothermic chemical reaction.

Next, completely stir again and transfer the mixture to another bottle, filtering it through a paper towel, cheese cloth, or other semi-permeable material to remove any remaining steel wool fibers. Let the filtered vinegar sit for several hours. The vinegar will acquire a strong amber color that will work as a wood stain. Additional vinegar can be

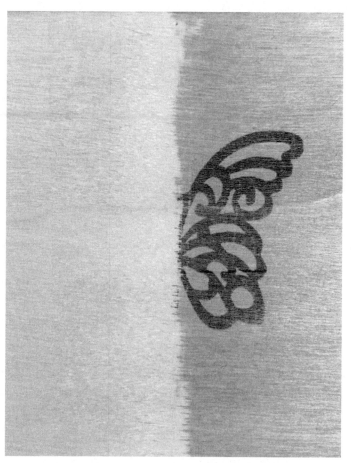

FIG. 3. *The borax mixture, which caused a uniform background darkening of the wood surface, intensified the power of the laser significantly, to the extent that there is no apparent engraving on the left side of the wood, although both sides were exposed to the same settings!*

FIG. 4. *A super fine steel wool pad, immersed in a mason jar filled with distilled white vinegar, will combine to form an effective wood stain.*

Laser Foil (colorful polyester laminate). Laser foil (non-PVC) can be applied over the surface of wood for the purpose of forming an image in a metallic color when exposed to the heat of a laser. The white paper backing on the foil is removed to reveal the adhesive layer, which is adhered to the wood. The white paper can be applied over the foil to prevent fumes from staining the foil during the engraving.

After engraving, the unwanted foil is removed and the remaining foil, which has formed the image, is burnished by placing the smooth side of the white paper over the work area, and applying pressure by a lateral movement (FIG. 6).

FIG. 5. *In less than two days the steel wool is partially dissolved and has changed color.*

FIG. 6. *Adhesive laser foil, available in a wide variety of metallic colors, can be laser-cut easily to produce attractive results.*

added to dilute the concentrated mixture to a preferred, lighter color. Experimenting with the proportion of concentrate can produce anything from a light gray to a dark brown affect. Each type of wood will react differently, and should be tested prior to committing to laser engraving.

Unlike commercially available wood stains, which add color to a wood, the vinegar/steel wool mixture chemically reacts with the wood surface causing it to oxidize. This chemical reaction makes the process somewhat unpredictable in regard to its effect on each type of wood. The oxidation also effects how the heat of the laser will darken the image.

The mixture is applied with a foam brush and dried completely before laser-engraving. Since the surface can be partially removed with a water-based sealer, an oil-based polyurethane should be applied after engraving to seal the surface.

The use of the stain can have two potential beneficial effects. First, it can darken and enhance the engraved image. Second, it can lessen the required laser power, or increase the processing speed.

Laser Defocusing. Purposefully running the laser out-of-focus can result in a darker image. An increase in the defocusing of the laser beam results in an increase of the laser spot size. This causes the laser to burn more of the wood surface, instead of passing off a portion of the energy in the form of vaporization. Because the laser is not perfectly focused the image will lose some of its details.

Post-treating Wood for a Darker and More Detailed Engraving

Laser Dark. Laser Dark (laserdark.com) is a semi-transparent aerosol coloring spray, that darkens a laser-engraved image on most types of wood, producing either a dark brown or dark black tone. It significantly increases the contrast and clarity of the image (FIG. 7).

FIG. 7. *Laser Dark, which was invented by Terry Biddle, owner of Awards and More in Eau Claire, WI, is used by professional award and plaque shops around the world. Credit: Laser Dark*

Prior to laser-engraving the wood surface must be covered with an adhesive paper mask to shield the non-image areas from the spray. The Laser Dark can must be shaken for at least one minute prior to use to ensure that the spray is adequately mixed. It is sprayed four to six inches from the engraved surface, moving back and forth, and releasing the valve at the end of each stroke. The material dries in one to three minutes, after which it is sprayed with a layer of Finish Coat, which requires from five to 15 minutes to completely dry. Within one hour the paper mask must be removed.

Producing a Detailed Image on Glass and Tile

Rust-Oleum Cold Galvanized Compound (Rust-Oleum 7585838 Spray Paint). This spray has a high zinc content that is evaporated by the heat of the laser to form a permanent high-contrast image on hard surfaces such as glass and ceramic tile. Use requires only a single spray coating, which dries faster than paint. After processing, the unexposed areas wash off with water, and light rubbing with steel wool.

Black Tempra Paint. Thoroughly clean the front and back glass surfaces with denatured alcohol to remove any surface dirt, dust, grease, or fingerprints. Pour some black tempra paint (FIG. 8) on the glass, spreading it evenly using a foam brush. Make sure the paint is completely dry. Position the glass with the paint side up. Be sure that the laser is focused on the workpiece surface. The laser will burn the paint, and mark the glass (FIG. 9). Wash off the remaining paint using tap water, rubbing with a paper towel or lint-free rag.

For a more uniform coat of tempra paint, mix equal parts of black tempra paint and water to a fluid consistency. Apply with an air brush using several light coats sprayed from side-to-side (FIG. 10).

As the laser strikes the tempra-coated surface it vaporizes the paint, revealing the surface below with its newly etched effect (FIG. 11)

FIG. 9. *The engraving process produces a visible image, clearly showing where the laser has burned off the paint.*

FIG. 8. *Crayola black tempra is an inexpensive, water-soluble paint that does an effective job of engraving on glass. Users have also reported success using white tempra paint.*

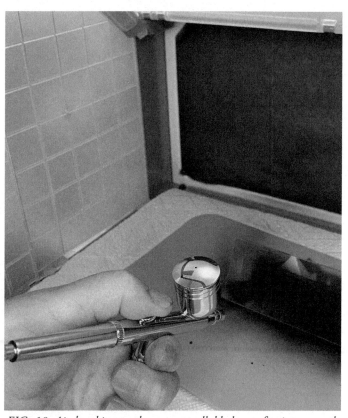

FIG. 10. *Air brushing produces a controllable layer of paint across the entire surface. A heavier coat will not necessarily produce a more dramatic engraving.*

FIG. 11. *The reaction of the laser heat with the dark tempra paint produces an attractive etched effect. An advantage of the tempra paint is that it easily cleans off with plain water. Note that glass is very sensitive to the relative intensity of the laser. If the laser is run too slowly it can result in the glass fracturing or cracking, ruining the piece. On the other hand, if the laser is run too fast it will result in either no image, or one that simply wipes off.*

FIG. 12. *The use of white spray paint, which contains titanium dioxide, reacts to the heat of a laser engraver to produce a permanent image. Users have had success using a variety of spray paint colors, as well as using two or more coats of different colors. Using a coating of black spray paint can also produce acceptable photographic image results, however the image will need to be prepared in negative format.*

A completed piece (FIG. 11) not only has a clearly visible image, but is etched below the surface, having fractured microscopic glass particles. The rough engraving can be felt, carefully, with a fingertip. The user should take care to clean the engraving completely to remove any remaining glass specks.

Rust-Oleum 2X White Ultracover Paint and Primer on Tile. Thoroughly clean a white ceramic tile with denatured alcohol, or acetone, and dry completely. Apply two light coats of white paint, spraying six to eight inches from the surface, moving back and forth, then up and down. Allow the paint adequate time to dry. Engrave the tile without air assist. The white paint turns black, creating a permanent image (FIG. 12). Clean the surface with acetone, and rub the surface with steel wool to remove any paint from the non-image areas. Wash with water and dry with a paper towel. This method is popularly known as the Norton White Tile Method (NWT), named after Nicky Norton.

Rust-Oleum 2X Flat Black Primer on Glass. Completely clean both sides of the glass until it is free of dust, dirt, and fingerprints. Lightly spray several coats of paint, moving back and forth across the surface.

Titanium Dioxide (TIO2). Materials that can be imaged using a layer of spray paint, can more effectively be imaged using a mixture of straight titanium dioxide, the active ingredient in spray paint that reacts to the heat of the laser. Titanium dioxide is the primary pigment used in the pharmaceutical, paint, and cosmetics industries

for its brilliant white opacity. Titanium dioxide can be purchased in powder form and mixed with alcohol in a 1 to 10 ratio, yielding a mixture that produces fewer fumes during processing than spray paint. During mixing the user must be sure that the TIO2 powder is free of lumps, and that the mixture is fluid and uniform.

For the most consistent coating the fluid should be applied with an airbrush (FIG. 13). Multiple light coats are best applied at a distance of six to eight inches from the surface, working in sweeping movements horizontally and then vertically. The applied powder should

FIG. 13. *This piece of glass was air-brushed with a titanium dioxide mixture and imaged with the laser engraver. A quick wash with water will reveal a clear detailed engraving.*

be handled carefully as it can wipe off and make the piece unusable. Other possible methods of application are paint brush, spray bottle, and pouring.

The laser engraving process is unremarkable except for the rather significant fact that titanium dioxide vapor may be hazardous if inhaled, and full attention should be paid to using adequate ventilation.

Following engraving, the surface of the substrate should be washed with water, and rubbed with a clean non-lint cloth to remove all of the excess TIO2 (FIG. 14).

FIG. 14. A finished piece of glass that was air-brush coated with titanium dioxide.

Laser Engraver Marking Paper. Laser engraver marking paper* is a specialty product that consists of a black plastic layer that is printed on a paper carrier sheet. A portion of the sheet is cut to a size slightly larger than the image area to be engraved. The glass, ceramic, or stone surface of the target material must be clean and dry. The marking paper material is soaked in water until its surface lifts from its carrier. It is then carefully peeled away from the paper backing and applied onto the object.

A rubber squeegee is used to carefully remove any air bubbles and surface imperfections from the surface. A hairdryer is used to set the material so that it is flat and dry.

The item is positioned in the laser engraver bed, or rotary, if it is cylindrical, and laser-engraved. When the engraving is complete, the item is soaked in clean, warm water until the marking paper lifts from the surface. The user can peel off any residual marking paper, then clean and dry the item. What remains is a well-defined image.

High Gloss Powder Coating. Powder coating, available in a wide variety of colors, is a finishing process that is usually applied using an electrostatic charge, and cured in an oven, steps that can not be used in a laser engraving environment.

_____
**Laser Engraver Marking Paper is available from xTool, https://tinyurl.com/47bxbz5s.*

Powder coating produces a hard, durable finish that is stronger, and usually thicker, than conventional painting methods. Powder coatings are typically used for car bodies, kitchen appliances, tools, and other items that are subject to hard wear, extreme temperature variations, and corrosive environments.

Powder coatings have a very small particle size, and are typically applied in a spray booth. Even in a laser-engraving environment, users must wear adequate protection to cover their eyes, nose, and mouth. In addition, latex gloves are strongly advised, as well as an apron to protect clothing.

The powder should not be sprayed, since none of the workpieces will likely accept an electrical charge to attract the powder, and hold it in place. Instead, the application of the powder must be managed physically, and very carefully.

Before the powder is applied, the workpiece surface, in this example a white ceramic tile, must be cleaned with alcohol or acetone, and dried completely. Next, it must be positioned on the laser bed and focused. Attempting to focus after the powder is applied will likely bring the laser shield, or possibly the laser head itself, in contact with the powder.

Attaining a thin uniform layer of powder is the main objective. There are three main ways to produce that. First, the powder can be placed in a fine mesh strainer and lightly applied (sifted) to the surface of the tile. The strainer is tapped lightly as it is moved across the surface of the tile to uniformly release as little powder as possible. The objective is to cover the tile in all places where it will be imaged.

The second way is to carefully cut off an ultra-thin strip from the bottom of an unneeded plastic credit card, leaving the original depth of the card intact on each end (FIG. 15). This creates a thin uni-

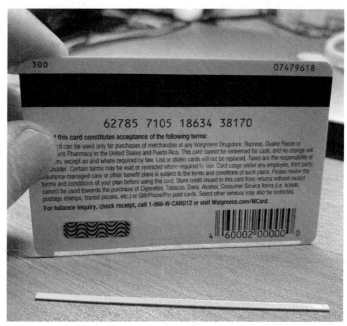

FIG. 15. A very narrow opening is cut into an unneeded plastic credit card to form a slot that will be used to spread a thin, even layer of powder coating material.

form opening that can be scraped across the surface of the workpiece to produce an even layer of powder. After the user applies a small amount of powder on the tile, the card is swept across the surface to produce a uniform layer of powder.

The workpiece must be handled extremely carefully since the powder can easily move and fall or blow into places it is not wanted.

As the heat of the laser penetrates the thin layer of colored powder coating, it melts and bonds the powder with the surface of the tile (FIG. 16). The interaction produces a hard, embossed image that rises slightly above the tile surface (FIG. 17).

The third application method is to apply a thin even layer of petroleum jelly to the surface of the workpiece, in this case, glass, after the glass has been cleaned with alcohol. The powder coating material is lightly sprinkled over the moist surface, and the glass is turned side-to-side to distribute it evenly. The piece is tapped lightly to remove the excess powder (FIG. 18). As the piece is engraved, the heat of the laser fuses the powder to the glass, producing a permanent image (FIG. 19). The excess powder is washed off and the glass is cleaned (FIG. 20).

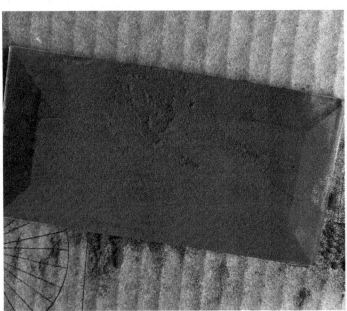

FIG. 18. A thin coat of petroleum jelly provides a firm base for the powder coat to adhere.

FIG. 16. The heat of the laser interacts with the powder coating to instantly harden it in the image areas. The excess powder will be recycled.

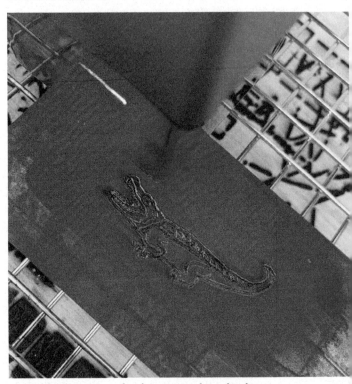

FIG. 19. The image is fused permanently to the glass.

FIG.17. The red powder coating, hardened by the heat of the laser, sits above the surface of the tile. Experimenting with other layer thicknesses, speeds, and power settings can produce a variety of other outcomes. This tile was produced on an xTool D1, speed 700mm/m, power 40.

Glass Frit. Glass frit is composed of finely crushed glass particles used in the making of fused glass, mainly for ornamentation (FIG. 21). Frit comes in a wide variety of colors and particle sizes.

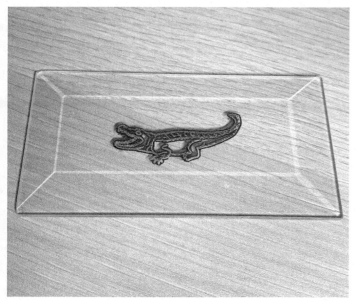

FIG. 20. The engraved alligator image retains a significant amount of the powder coating color.

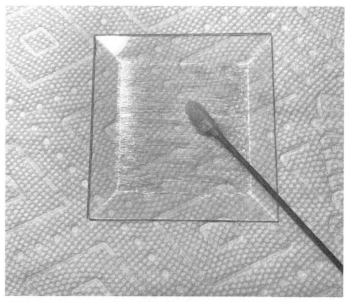

FIG. 22. A thin coat of petroleum jelly serves to hold the frit in a uniform layer for engraving.

Frit can be used to image on glass by simply applying it to the surface of the workpiece. The gritty powder can be applied to a piece of glass by spreading a thin layer of petroleum jelly on the surface (FIG. 22), sifting the frit over it so that it is completely covered, and then shaking off the excess (FIG. 23). The thin layer of frit is sufficient to engrave the surface (FIG. 24).

After engraving, the area exposed to the laser can be clearly seen (FIG. 25). The finished engraving has some remnants of the frit embedded in the glass (FIG. 26).

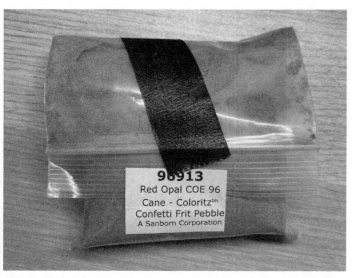

FIG. 21. Glass frit is available from many online sources as well as from local glass studios. For purposes of engraving on glass, the finer the frit texture the better.

FIG. 23. After spooning a quantity of frit over the petroleum jelly surface the glass can be tapped to remove the excess.

FIG. 24. The frit-coated glass is ready for engraving.

FIG. 25. The area exposed to the laser has fused with the surface. All evidence of the color has been absorbed by the heat.

FIG. 26. The tiny frit particles have permanently fused with the glass surface. A colorant can be applied to accentuate the contrast.

Post-treating Material for a Darker and More Detailed Engraving

Black Shoe Polish. Black shoe polish, preferably with a sponge dabber top, can darken an engraved image on MDF, a coated wood surface (FIG. 27). The polish is dabbed on a portion of the image, going over it twice, but not letting it dry. The excess should be lightly rubbed off using a soft cloth moistened with alcohol. This process is repeated until all of the polish in the background has been completely removed. Repeat until the entire image area has been treated.

FIG. 27. Black shoe polish, available in a variety of formulations, can be used to darken an image on smooth engraved surfaces such as MDF. For best results the surface should be sealed with a clear coat spray to keep the black dye from seeping into the wood surface. https://tinyurl.com/5y86sabn

Marsh Stencil Ink. Marsh stencil ink, available in an aerosol spray, is applied to an engraved surface that has already been masked with paper masking material, or sprayed with multiple coats of clear acrylic spray (FIG. 28). If it is used with a paper mask it requires no preparation of the material surface. The stencil spray, which is an ink rather than a paint, provides a deep, dark image with little risk of bleeding beyond the image areas. It dries fast and is set by spraying with a clear spray sealer.

FIG. 29. *In order to return the MDF to its natural color, the surface needed to be sanded. Half of the MDF was taped off to show the difference that sanding would make.*

FIG. 28. *The entire surface of this piece of MDF was sprayed with clear acrylic to seal the surface prior to engraving. Despite this protective layer, the stencil ink partially clung to the surface.*

FIG. 30. *The left side has been sanded down to its original surface color. The Marsh stencil ink remains as a dark contrast in the recesses of the engraving. After sanding, the fine sawdust was removed using a dry air brush.*

After cleaning with acetone, a film of the stencil ink may remain. A light sanding using an orbital hand sander removes the remaining stencil ink (FIG. 29). The sanded surface provides a good contrast to the dark impression of the stencil ink (FIG. 30).

Marking Steel Surfaces

Dry Moly Lube. Dry Moly Lube, or Moly Lube (molybdenum disulfide) is a gray-to-black coating that provides a layer of lubrication that persists even under extreme conditions. Using two to three coats, each drying completely between applications, it has been shown to support laser marking on stainless steel with a 20W laser diode, such as the Ortur (FIG. 31). After processing, the excess spray can be removed with acetone. This spray has also been shown to work on glass.

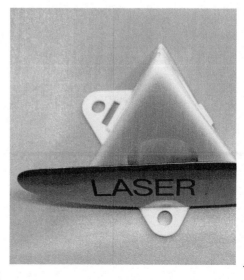

FIG. 31. *Dry Moly Lube produces a utility-grade image, however the harm it can cause to the laser engraver and the user's health are important negative factors.*

Enduramark. Enduramark was founded by Ryan Huddleston and Jason Fink in response to a need to laser-engrave water bottles for a sporting-goods company Ryan owned. The demand for personalized items led Ryan to buy a CO2 laser, and become expert in all aspects of the laser-engraving business. Ryan's master's degree in organic chemistry, and experience with supplying specialty chemicals to the pharmaceutical industry, led to his formulation of a line of marking sprays for CO2 and diode laser engravers.

Enduramark formulations are based on molybdenum oxide, as opposed to molybdenum disulfide, the main ingredient in Molylube (Dry Moly Lube) spray, which is often used as an inexpensive metal-marking substitute. Although Molylube can be used for metal marking, it contains sulfur, which produces sulfuric acid when burned in a laser. Over time the corrosive effects of the acid will damage virtually every component in the laser engraver, as well as pose a serious health hazard to the user. In addition, Molylube, developed as a lubricant, is particularly difficult to wash off, and does not produce a reliably uniform mark.

Each can of Enduramark comes with an additional nozzle, so that in the unlikely event of a clog, the user can continue working. Also included are general directions for spraying and suggested laser settings (FIG. 32).

Black Laser Marking Spray. Enduramark Black Laser Marking Spray produces a solid, permanent, uniform black image when exposed to proper laser power (FIG. 33). The durability of the image has been tested under severe weather conditions, for over 1000 hours, with no observable degradation. The engraved image has also been shown to tolerate scratch resistance, organic solvents, and caustic chemicals with little to no change.

The spray is particularly uniform, resulting in a consistently solid black laser engraving result on uncoated stainless steel, ferrous metals, brass, titanium, zinc, brass, and nickel. The unexposed material is rinsed off with tap water.

Enduramark recommends applying a thin coat, and running the laser at high power and slow speed, with a dpi of 300.

Black Laser Marking Paste. Black Laser Marking Paste is combined with denatured alcohol to produce a uniform mixture that can be applied with an airbrush, paint brush, or Preval sprayer.

FIG. 32. The Enduramark Black is formulated for uncoated stainless steel, while the Enduramark Charcoal is made for glass and ceramic.

Charcoal Laser Marking Spray. Enduramark Charcoal Laser Marking Spray is formulated for laser engraving on glass and ceramic (FIG. 34). It produces a permanent, uniform charcoal mark that has been thoroughly tested for image uniformity and durability. After engraving, the material in the non-exposed areas is removed by rinsing with water.

Enduramark recommends applying a thick coating that completely covers the object. The suggested power lever is high, with a high speed for glass, a moderate speed for ceramic, and a dpi of 600.

FIG. 33. The Enduramark Black Laser Marking Spray, which requires only a thin coating, produces a clear, dense, black image.

FIG. 34. The Enduramark Charcoal Laser Marking Spray produces a sharp well-defined image on glass or ceramic. This piece of stained glass has a very light wispy layer of white dispersed through its surface.

LaserBond 100. LaserBond 100 (laserbondingtech.com) is a recognized leader in the category of professional all-purpose laser marking sprays and inks. It has been scientifically formulated, using sub-micron and nanoparticle materials, to bond to hard surfaces, such as metal, glass, and ceramic, to produce a permanent, black, well-defined image. Tested metals include stainless steel, brass, aluminum, copper, titanium, tin, nickel, and many others.

It has been used successfully in a wide range of industries to mark such things as auto parts, dinnerware, catalytic converters, space station components, kitchen appliance panels, windshields, pharma vials, and many, many more.

LaserBond 100 works by absorbing laser energy, creating the level of heat necessary to create a covalent molecular bond with hard inorganic surfaces. Unlike other laser marking technologies, LaserBond 100 adds material to the substrate surface rather than removing or altering it.

LaserBond 100 is similar to other commercial surface marking products, such as TherMark, CerMark, and Enduramark. According to LaserBond 100, it has a number of competitive advantages in that its nanoparticle technology marks uniformly on a wide variety of different surfaces; its smaller particle size and thin coating provides up to 2,500 sq. in. of coverage per spray can; its smaller particle size results in more efficient laser energy absorption producing faster laser marking speeds; unexposed areas rinse off with tap water, and since it contains no environmentally hazardous chemicals the run-off can go directly down the drain; and finally, it ican be less expensive than competitive products.

LaserBond 100 has an impressive pedigree, having been developed by Paul W. Harrison, the inventor of the laser bonding process, and founder or TherMark LLC. Mr. Harrison was the first to use a laser, rather than a conventional oven or kiln, to porcelainize pots, pans, and cast-iron sinks, as well as to decorate china and crystal.

Available in both an aerosol spray can and liquid ink (FIG. 35), the material is applied to the target surface, dried for a few minutes, engraved, and then washed with water.

The spray can must be shaken for at least one minute prior to use. The user should make sure that he or she hears the metal ball inside the can move up and down, indicating that the contents is being mixed. After the spraying session has concluded, the can must be turned upside down, and the nozzle pressed for a few seconds, to clear any remaining material from the valve.

A thin, even, smooth coating is recommended for producing a high-quality, dark mark. A thicker coat will require increased laser power and will result in decreased marking resolution. The can should be held about eight-to-ten inches from the workpiece, slowly moved from side to side, applying an even, smooth and thin coating.

The spray air dries in about two minutes, although the drying time can be decreased by using a hair dryer, heat gun, or heat lamp. The processed image has been fully tested to resist both physical and chemical exposure, high temperature, and mechanical abrasion.

Although LaserBond has been thoroughly tested with CO2 lasers, the author has found it an excellent pre-treatment for metal, glass, and ceramic using a diode laser, such as the xTool D1 (FIG. 36), (FIG. 37), (FIG. 38), (FIG. 39).

FIG. 36. The smooth coating of the LaserBond 100 spray on glass has successfully accepted the heat of the xTool D1 laser. This photo is just prior to washing the surface with water.

FIG. 35. The LaserBond 100 spray is applied from six to eight inches from the surface using a back and forth motion. The LaserBond 100 ink must be diluted with denatured alcohol at least one-to-one, and applied with a foam brush, or a two-to-one dilution using an airbrush or spray gun. Credit: LaserBond 100.

FIG. 37. The laser-engraved glass surface following a quick rinse with water. The unexposed LaserBond 100 easily washed off without the need for scrubbing.

FIG. 38. The LaserBond 100 produced a clear, crisp, black image on a white ceramic tile. Post-processing with water was quick and easy.

Black Shoe Dye. Black shoe dye does not provide a good, even layer of dense, dark coating for engraving (FIG. 40). However, it is very inexpensive, and although the marking quality is mediocre, it may suffice for jobs that are more utilitarian than decorative.

FIG. 39. This solid black image on a stainless steel butter knife is among the best results on metal of any pre-treatment method tested in this book.

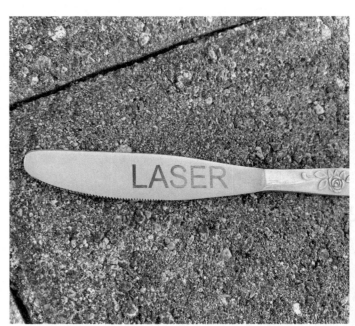

FIG. 40. Although black shoe polish does produce a visible image, and is low-cost, the results are rather sub-standard. The liquid dye does not cover evenly and the results are proof of that.

Food Safe Finishes

A common laser engraved surface is a wooden cutting board. Cutting boards, and other items that come in close contact with food, must be finished with a lead-free coating that is properly cured. Finishes generally require 30 days to totally cure at room temperature (65 to 75 degrees F). Although it is best to look for finishes that are labeled "food or salad-bowl safe," which do not contain driers, and take quite a while to dry, the Food and Drug Administration approves of the oil and varnishes used to speed the curing time. According to an article in *American Woodworker,* June, 2002, issue #94: "There is no evidence that today's driers are unsafe. No case of poisoning from finishes containing these driers has ever been reported. The Food and Drug Administration approves the use of these driers in coatings, and no warnings are required on cans or Material Data Safety Sheets."

An alternative to finishes that require significant curing times is Hope's Tung Oil (FIG. 41).

FIG. 41. Hope's Tung Oil is a natural wood finish and sealer that is rubbed on, and cures at room temperature. The finish penetrates into wood fibers, becoming a flexible non-oily solid that bonds with the wood. When dry, it is non-toxic, and is recommended for cutting boards and other surfaces that come in contact with food. https://amzn.to/37L-5wU4. Credit: Amazon

Removing Surface Residue on Powder-Coated Metal and Wood

Mr. Clean Magic Eraser. Stains, scorches, and other residue are sometimes formed on wood following cutting, or on a powder-coated metal surface following engraving.

A powder-coated metal surface can be cleaned of any remaining sticky residue with a small amount of a commercial degreaser cleaner, such as *LA's Totally Awesome All-Purpose Concentrated Cleaner,* sprayed on the surface, left to work for a few seconds, and polished with an eraser sponge. The small amount of pumice in the melamine foam eraser combined with the cleaner, cleans and intensifies the brilliance of the metal surface. Alternately the sprayed surface can be wiped with a lint-free rag or micro-fabric cloth.

Other degreasers shown to work effectively in removing sticky residue are *Zep Fast 505 Industrial Cleaner & Degreaser,* and *Goof Off Heavy Duty Remover.* Pay attention to any handling and use warnings on all product labels.

Alternately, a second pass of the laser will usually burn off any sticky residue, however, it results in doubling the processing time.

Laser cutting of detailed work on wood can result in significant laser heat concentrated most specifically on the back side, causing scorch-

ing and staining. A dampened lint-free cloth can remove some of the problem, however, a dampened magic eraser will remove most, if not all, of the remaining burnt discoloration.

White Vinegar. An effective solution for removing slightly burnt or discolored surface markings, ash or soot, or sticky surface residue from wood is white vinegar. It can be poured over the wood surface and worked in with a stiff bristle brush. The surface can be rinsed in water and dried immediately with paper towels. The wood must be dried evenly to avoid warping.

Sanding
The sanding process releases tiny airborne particles that can irritate eyes and enter the respiratory system. Users should wear appropriate safety equipment at all times, and be aware of environmental dangers.

Prior to Engraving. Sanding is not an intuitive process, since to the naked eye, most commercially available wood looks smooth, and ready to use. Despite the fact that sanding is noisy, dirty, and time-consuming, it is an important part of the laser engraving workflow.

The process of sanding removes a thin layer of wood by scratching its surface with a sustained light pressure. The size of the scratches is dependent on the grit of the sandpaper…the higher the grit, the higher the number of granules of sand per square inch, the finer the scratches. The objective is to have no visible scratches, blemishes, or uneven surfaces. The scratches affect how the laser will react with the surface, and how stain and other pre/post treatments will appear.

One method that ensures that sanding has been uniformly applied, is to scribble a light pencil line across the entire wood surface. Next use a light sanding pressure, in the direction of the grain, across the board until the pencil line is no longer visible.

If multiple applications of sanding are to be used, start with the lower grit, i.e. coarser sandpaper and work progressively to a higher grit. Remove any sawdust between grit changes to avoid sawdust clogging the next higher grit paper. The life of sandpaper can be extended by using an abrasive cleaning stick that removes surface debris from the paper, disc, or belt https://amzn.to/3FL9OaF.

Scratches are minimized by sanding in the direction of the grain, or the way that the wood fibers align. This is because scratches made in the grain direction tend to blend in, and are less noticeable. On the other hand, scratches made against the grain are very obvious and difficult to remove.

In addition to using a vacuum or compressed air, sandpaper dust can be easily, and effectively, removed from a wood surface using a dusting sheet, such as a Swiffer Sweeper. The static cleaning nature of the sheets readily attracts the dust. Professional woodworkers also use a tac cloth, which is slightly sticky, and attracts the finest particles.

After Engraving. Burnt or heavily sooted engraved surfaces may benefit from an application of denatured alcohol, applied with a lint-free cloth prior to sanding. Wipe the alcohol in the direction of the wood grain. The alcohol easily removes surface residue and will reduce the amount of time required for sanding.

Raw, or unsealed wood, that has not received any surface treatment from the mill, can be sanded after engraving, provided that the nature of the engraving consists only of a low-detailed, black-and-white graphic (not grayscale nor photograph). The user should use settings that result in a deep engraving, since the surface will be sanded. Unlike pretreated wood surfaces, that can be wiped clean of unwanted engraving residue using a dry cloth, an untreated engraved wood needs a physical abrasion, i.e. sanding, to remove heat staining. The sanding is accomplished using an orbital sander with up to 220 grit sandpaper. Sanding continues only until the laser stains have been removed. Finish by blowing off the sawdust with compressed air or by using a vacuum. Tiny sanded wood particles can get caught in the engraved recesses and become problematic if using a stain or spray finish.

After Staining or Finishing. Wood is typically sanded before staining in order to remove any surface imperfections that would become more obvious with the application of a stain. After staining or finishing, wood is often sanded lightly to remove any incidental dust that may have dried into the surface, and to knock down any fibers that are sticking up. The sanding also helps any additional coats of sealer to adhere to the previous one.

Note that oil-based stains are combustible, and could possibly catch fire. For that reason, water-based stains are preferable.

Finishing and Sealing

Laser engraved projects, such as signs, may not necessarily need to be finished nor sealed if they remain indoors. However, the harsh conditions of the outdoors, with rain and snow, heat and cold, driving winds and other hazards, make surface treatment a definite requirement. A wood finish, or sealer, adds a layer of protection from moisture, spills, scratches, stains, and UV damage, as well as enhances the appearance and tactile feel.

Any laser engraved wooden workpiece attains its image by directing the heat of the laser onto the surface of the wood. The result is an image that is some shade of brown. The contrast between the burnt image, and the native wood surface, determines how easy it is to see the message or design. Darkening the wood with the use of a stain usually decreases the image contrast, and may detract from the overall effectiveness and beauty of the piece. So, the application of a wood finish may be less important than the application of a sealer.

Sealing to prevent burn marks. Spraying or painting a quick-drying wood sealer on the wood surface can help reduce burn marks. It needs to be thoroughly dry before proceeding. The engraving process can leave sticky scorch marks and surface debris, that can be cleaned with a small amount of denatured alcohol applied to a clean lint-free cloth and wiped in the direction of the wood grain. Optionally, to reveal more detail, the entire surface can be sanded with a high-grit sandpaper in the grain direction. Compressed air or a vacuum should be used to remove the resulting sawdust. At this point a finishing stain or sealer can be applied.

Cleaning scorched surfaces and edges. Prior to sealing, a light coating of Orange Goop Waterless hand cleaner (available at Amazon,

(https://amzn.to/3MhbDyF) can be worked into the areas with soot, scorch, and discoloration, and rubbed gently with a small soft brush, such as a toothbrush. The residue can be removed with a paper towel. Once the surface has been sealed there is no going back to remediate surface flaws and laser residue.

Soot and ash can also be removed by brushing the surface with a stiff bristle brush, moving across the surface with a light circular motion to avoid breaking off small engraved details.

A last resort option to removing burnt residue is washing the piece under running water, while rubbing lightly to ensure that the burnt particles wash away. A small amount of mild soap can be applied if necessary. Wetting the wood makes the fibers swell, possibly warping the surface; so it is important to quickly and properly dry the piece.

Adding a protective spray. Using a lacquer, varnish, or clear coat spray seals the surface of the wood providing a layer of protection from dirt, handling, and the environment. Prior to spraying, the user must be sure that the wood surface is clean so that impurities are not sealed into the wood.

The user should carefully investigate the characteristics of the products to be used to coat the wood. Some are water-based, some oil-based; some are glossy, some are matte. Some are combo-based, with a stain and sealant in a single product. An excellent guide to woodworking finishes can be found at https://tinyurl.com/msak684p.

The presence of a burnt surface may, in some cases, add an attractive, rustic visual appearance to a piece. If that is the case, the user can refrain from any finishing operations.

Embossing Powder. Embossing powder can add a colorful, glossy, sheen to the surface of a laser-cut piece (FIG. 42). Embossing powders, available in a wide variety of colors and metallics, easily adhere

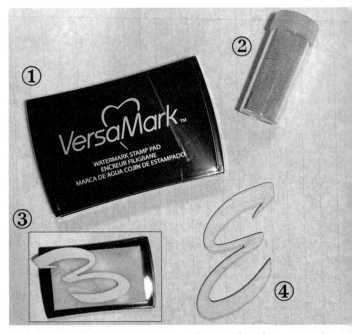

FIG. 42. 1. *The VersaMark stamp pad. 2. Pink embossing powder. 3. The surface of the laser-cut "E" rubbed on the stamp pad. 4. The top of the laser-cut "E" with the adhesive applied.*

to a wooden piece that has a thin layer of adhesive applied on its surface. A common means of applying the adhesive is with a VersaMark embossing stamp pad (https://amzn.to/3PybGIq).

A laser-cut piece that has been covered with adhesive readily accepts the embossing powder, which has been liberally applied to its surface (FIG. 43). The piece is carefully lifted, and the excess is removed and poured back into the container.

FIG. 44. The melted embossing powder is exposed to intense heat to form a permanent hard surface.

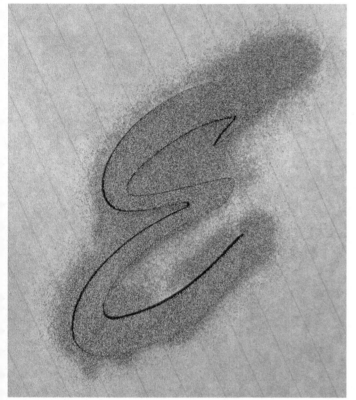

FIG. 43. The embossing powder is poured over the surface of the laser-cut piece so that the entire area is completely covered. The excess is shaken off and returned to the embossing powder bottle.

The laser-cut piece, with its coating of embossing powder, is exposed to the heat of a mini heat gun (https://amzn.to/3ld4m6U). The heat is gradually run along the surface, moving slowing, until the powder melts to form a hard coat (FIG. 44).

Epoxy Resin
Epoxy resin, sometimes referred to as casting resin, laminating resin, synthetic resin, or simply, resin, is available from many manufacturers, and made to fulfill a wide variety of applications.

Epoxy resin used for laser engraving, like most resins, consists of two liquid parts, resin and hardener, usually mixed 1:1. When combined, the mixture radiates heat; and in time, usually over a period of 24 hours, the two parts are converted from a liquid to a solid. In its cured state the resin is clear and hard, and protects the surface to which it has been applied, from scratching, chipping, and discoloring. Epoxy resin is the ultimate form of a clear coat, far exceeding the protection of a clear coat spray.

Note that the use of epoxy resin, in rare circumstances, can cause skin irritation; and users should always wear disposable nitrile gloves to reduce the possibility of exposure to the skin.

The use of epoxy resin in the realm of laser engraving is usually confined to filling, coating, or a combination of both.

Filling. Epoxy resin, with its hard, shiny surface, and its capacity to combine with a wide variety of colorants, makes it an attractive choice for filling-in openings made by a laser cutter. Laser-cut openings can be formed for a wide variety of purposes, including jewelry, wall hangings, decorative plaques, signs, and many more (FIG. 45).

After laser cutting, the workpiece may undergo further treatment, such as wood accepting a stain, or MDF accepting paint. A piece of clear adhesive vinyl is then adhered to the back of the workpiece, so that the epoxy does not leak out the back of the cut-out areas. After processing and hardening, the vinyl can be removed. The user must ensure that the workpiece is level on the work surface so that the fill is evenly distributed. The mixed epoxy resin is carefully poured into the cut-outs, or, if the opening is particularly small, applied drop-by-drop using a wood craft pick (https://amzn.to/3yJfOzn). Depending on the design intent, the resin may be restricted to being level with the top surface of the piece, or may both fill the openings, and coat the surface. In either case, trapped air bubbles must be removed by carefully moving a heat gun or lighted torch slowly over the resin surface.

Coating. Epoxy resin can be applied to any surface to provide a protective coating that is not only attractive, but one that enhances the strength and durability of the base material. For materials such as basswood, which is often very thin, and subject to cracking and breaking, the addition of a surface coating not only seals in the surface color, but provides a clear, hard shield (FIG. 46). In most cases it is not necessary to apply a pre-coat sealant in order to avoid absorption into the workpiece. If there is any concern, the user should first apply some epoxy resin to a scrap piece of material for experimentation.

FIG. 45. A piece of clear plastic adhesive was placed over the back of this cut-out of a palm tree to retain the liquid epoxy. The cut-out was filled in with ArtResin (www.artresin.com) epoxy tinted with ArtResin ResinTint green.

FIG. 46. This coaster was produced with an inset application of green epoxy resin for the palm tree. After the inset was dry, a clear top coat was applied to the entire surface.

Small articles, such as beads, stones, ornaments or decorative bric-a-brac, can be added after the first thin layer of the epoxy resin has been poured into the laser cut-outs. After two-to-four hours, the user can

complete the resin coverage, remove any surface air bubbles, and let the resin dry.

When working with a cutting or charcuterie board, or any item that will come in contact with food, the user should apply the epoxy resin, let it dry, sand it, and apply a final top coat. Not all epoxy resins are food safe. A food safe epoxy is inert when cured, and will not leach any chemicals into food that comes in contact with it.

Any epoxy resin can be enhanced with the addition of acrylic paint, alcohol ink, mica or metallic powders, tints, glitter, and other colorants. ArtResin ResinTint is non-toxic and non-flammable, and made specifically for mixing with ArtResin epoxy resins. A general rule of thumb is to add approximately 6% of a colorant to the volume of epoxy resin for proper color coverage.

The addition of a colorant will likely compromise the food safe status of an epoxy resin coating. If a workpiece has been coated with a mixture containing a colorant, and the piece is to be used in contact with food, the user should apply a final topcoat of non-tinted food-safe epoxy resin.

ArtResin (http://artresin.com), used in these examples, is non-toxic and non-flammable, BPA-free, and provides superior protection against the yellowing effects of UV light.

Masks

The purpose of a mask is to shield the surface of a material for at least one of two reasons. First, it can prevent errant laser energy, resulting in the form of soot, singe, or discoloration, from forming around the outlines of vector images engraved specifically in wood. Second, it can allow for the addition of color, or the topical application of a finish or stain in virtually any material, solely to the specific areas where the mask has been burned away. The remaining mask keeps any surface application from filling in the non-image areas.

The common masks used in laser engraving are blue painter's tape and paper masking material. Regardless of the composition of the material, it must be applied firmly, and secured to the substrate surface using a brayer, roller, squeegee, or burnisher.

Painter's tape, like all masking tapes, is made with a crepe paper backing onto which an adhesive is applied. Generally, blue painters tape has a medium tack; green painter's tape has a high tack. Paper masking material has a smoother finish, but like painter's tape has a layer of adhesive that holds the material to the surface to which it is applied, preventing anything that is brushed on the surface, following laser engraving, to seep beyond its edges. Both types of masks peel off easily, leaving no residue. Other masking materials, such as those used for sandblasting and air erasing, are made of polyester.

Painter's Tape. Painter's tape, available in a variety of widths, is generally available in narrow rolls, and used typically for small-scale jobs. It usually has a medium-tack adhesive, and is easily burned off when exposed to the heat of a laser. The user should avoid overlapping the tape since this changes, ever so slightly, the distance of the laser and the wood surface, and can leave noticeable imaging anomalies, such as banding.

Paper Masking Material. Paper masking material is generally available in wider widths, and with lower tack, than painter's tape. It provides a protective layer when cutting and engraving, and prevents edge burn marks on all sorts of materials.

Both painter's tape and paper masking material can be used to restrict the application of paint to add color to a vector engraving. Paint can only enter areas that have been engraved by the heat of the laser, the heat having burned off the masking material only in the imaged areas (FIG. 47). The application of paint provides an added dimension of contrast which can be a welcome break from the default scorch/burnt brown produced by the laser.

FIG. 48. *This masking technique has restricted the application of blue acrylic paint to the right side of the butterfly wing.*

In order to overcome the dark image imposed by the laser, the user may opt to use a white base coat as a primer, to allow the true color of the paint to show (FIG. 49). By diminishing the brown/black impression of the engraving the finished surface is truer to its intent (FIG. 50)

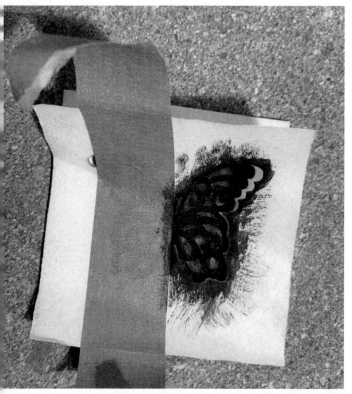

FIG. 47. *This piece of basswood has been covered with a piece of paper masking material and then engraved with an image of a butterfly. It was then partially masked with blue painter's tape on the left, to mask the left side of the butterfly. The engraved (i.e. burnt) parts of the butterfly wing exposed the wood for receiving the blue paint, which, due to the protective paper mask, only adhered to the exposed image. Here you can see the mask has been partially removed, showing that the excess paint is on the mask rather than on the wood.*

Prior to engraving, the user may want to spray the wood surface with a varnish, a polyurethane or clear acrylic, and let it dry completely. The varnish, in addition to providing a slightly glossy surface, helps to prevent paint, stain, or whatever colorant is used, from seeping beyond the image areas.

After engraving the burnt away areas, representing the image, the exposed areas are covered with the colorant, such as acrylic paint (FIG. 48). The colorant must be completely dry before removing the masking material. If any of the colorant has bled, it can be removed with a fine grit sandpaper to restore the clean outlines of the image.

FIG. 49. *In order to accentuate the paint color, and present it as a truer color, the user can first apply a layer of white acrylic paint.*

The colored image, and surrounding area, can be protected with a final application of clear coat spray.

Liquid Masks

Paper and tape masking materials can suffer from three main deficiencies: First, the adhesive may not be strong enough to stay in

FIG. 50. With the addition of a primer coat of white, the red acrylic maintains its true color.

FIG. 51. The Laser ProtectMask 5900 solution can be applied easily to almost any substrate and stored for months until needed.

FIG. 52. After the laser has removed the ProtectMask coating from the image areas, a colorant can be applied.

place, and may lift, or peel; second, regardless of its adhesion, applying it to a semi-porous material, like most woods, will not stop a color treatment from seeping under the material, minimizing the effectiveness of the mask; third, the adhesive on a paper or tape mask may lift off a layer of the substrate when removed, especially on leather, or may leave behind residue from the adhesive. Although not a perfect solution in all cases, a liquid mask has the potential to temporarily bond with the surface it is applied to, reaching into any imperfections in the substrate surface.

Another benefit of a liquid mask is that it can protect uneven, textured surfaces, or odd shapes, which might be difficult or impossible for adhesive-based papers, tapes, or films. Users should check to be sure that a liquid mask product does not contain PVC, which can produce toxic fumes.

Laser ProtectMask 5900. Laser ProtectMask 5900, made by General Chemical Corporation (https://generalchem.com/category/laser-engraving), is a peelable liquid masking solution made specifically for professional laser engraving. It is safe to handle, non-flammable, and particularly easy to remove, peeling off in sheets rather than messy flakes.

The material is fairly viscous, and can be applied to almost any substrate with a foam or bristle brush, or porous or solid roller (FIG. 51). Drying time averages about twenty minutes, although it can be hastened with the use of heat lamps or exposure to sunlight. Coated surfaces can be safely stored for months, and used when necessary. After curing, the mask provides a particularly strong and uniform film that restricts the energy of the laser to its intended image areas (FIG. 52). The mask eliminates harmful and unattractive smoke discoloration, and serves as a precision mask for adding color (FIG. 53).

A number of commercial art supplies, developed to mask areas of a painting, or parts of a model, have been successfully used to mask laser engraving projects. These include:

Liquitex Masking Fluid. Liquitex Masking Fluid is a colorless non-toxic, latex-based fluid. The thickness and contour of the brush or applicator, determines the level of detail that can be achieved Engraving can commence as soon as the solution has dried. The laser

FIG. 53. After the ProtectMask coating has been removed, only the color image remains in the engraved areas.

removes the mask, leaving the image areas exposed on the surface of the substrate. At this point the user applies the colorant using a method most appropriate for the specific material. It may be advisable to apply the color in multiple thin layers to avoid seeping. After the final layer of color has dried, the mask is removed by rubbing it lightly with the corner of a crafter's eraser (https://amzn.to/3M-lP8Zi), also known as a crepe eraser, or a clean finger. The mask should lift off easily leaving little or no trace nor residue.

Grumbacher Miskit Liquid Frisket. Grumbacher Miskit Liquid Frisket, made of natural rubber latex, is distinguished by its bright fluorescent orange color, which helps to identify its presence in contrast with the substrate surface.

Grafix WM2 White Mask Liquid Frisket. Grafix WM2 White Mask Liquid Frisket is a white latex mask that is sufficiently fluid to be airbrushed.

Gold Leaf Sheets

Gold leaf sheets, either real gold or imitation (https://amzn.to/3Mh-diEp), can express a bright, brilliant, gleaming metallic surface effect (FIG. 54). The sheets, exceptionally thin and delicate, can be laser-cut and applied to another surface using an adhesive. Some users have had success gluing the leaf to a masked workpiece and then lasering (FIG. 55).

FIG. 55. When gold leaf is to be applied to a workpiece it requires a special glue, such as Speedball Mona Lisa Metal Leaf Adhesive (https://amzn.to/37Lnu8X). The glue, which applies with a brush, dries in about 30 minutes, although the drying time can be reduced with the use of heat gun. Excess glue, outside the defined work area can be cleaned with soap and water. Credit: Amazon

One way, and certainly the most difficult way to use an individual gold leaf, is to sandwich it between the two slip-sheets of paper that it is packaged with, and carefully set it on the laser bed. Using a low power, and a reasonably fast speed, and NO air assist, a design is cut into the leaf. Removing the cut-out and transferring it to another surface is extremely delicate and precise work. The receiving piece must have an adhesive layer applied to hold the gold leaf. This process can be exasperating, since it is very difficult to control the movement and placement of gold leaf, and once any part of the leaf touches the adhesive surface it cannot be moved.

Another method, which is considerably easier, is to adhere the gold leaf sheet to a piece of adhesive-back paper, and then commence the laser-cutting (FIG. 56). The cut pieces can then be glued to another surface as needed (FIG. 57).

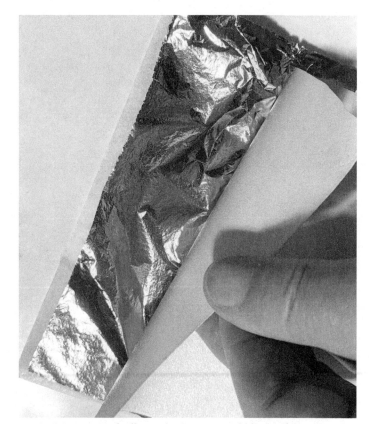

FIG. 54. These imitation gold leaf sheets, made primarily of copper, are packaged between thin sheets of tissue paper. The extraordinary thinness of the leaves makes them particularly difficult and frustrating to work with. Credit: Amazon

FIG. 56. A piece of adhesive-back paper, with the backing removed, is very carefully placed over a sheet of gold leaf material and burnished. The paper adds to the stability of the gold leaf making it easier to handle, position, cut, and ultimately adhere to a workpiece.

FIG. 57. This series of characters was cut from a sheet of gold leaf that was adhered to a piece of adhesive-backed paper.

Adding Color without a Mask

1 Shot Sign Painter's Lettering Enamel. This oil-based enamel paint has, since its introduction in 1948, distinguished itself for its exceptional one-coat coverage, even layering, and durable, vibrant gloss finish.

This engraving, produced using tempra paint, is ready to receive a coat of white paint to help the image stand out (FIG. 58). Although it can be applied with almost any brush, a stencil brush, with moderate-

ly stiff bristles, is best at moving the paint into tiny surface recesses (FIG. 59). The excess paint is removed before it can dry, adhering only to the recesses of the engraving (FIG. 60).

FIG. 59. The 1 Shot Sign Paint must be generously applied in order to fill all of the engraved recesses.

FIG. 58. A prospective surface must have a sufficiently deep engraving to receive the 1 Shot Sign Paint.

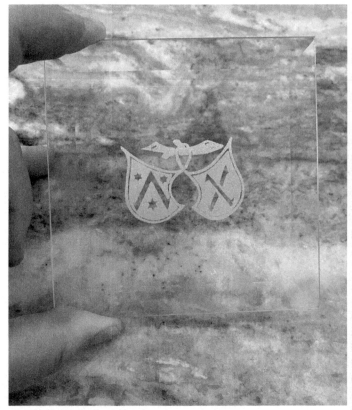

FIG. 60. The finished glass surface has a durable high-gloss white coating.

16. Summary: Laser Engraver Buyer's Guide

The popularity of laser engraving and cutting, driven by its affordability, ease-of-use, and creative applications, has encouraged a growing number of manufacturers to enter the field. For the potential user, selecting the right laser engraver/cutter has become a complicated decision when all of the critical factors are taken into account. For those contemplating a purchase it is important to know what features to look for, how the machine will meet their individual needs, now and in the future, and what is the user support system that they may be joining?

Two of the most popular open-frame laser engravers presently marketed are the Ortur Laser Master 2 Pro and the xTool D1. Both are excellent choices. Between them they represent the complete range of features that distinguish the category of diode laser engravers. These devices have developed a mature user base due to their distinctive capabilities, competitive pricing, and vendor support.

These two laser engraver/cutters are representative of the typical open-frame design of a low-cost machine. New to the design of a laser engraver is the xTool M1, which is a self-contained, dual-function device covered in its own chapter. It defines a new generation of machine.

Here is a list of the major elements that should be considered when making a purchase decision:

Assembly

Laser engravers are usually shipped in pieces...they are not completely assembled and ready for use out-of-the-box. The exception is the xTool M1, which is shipped totally assembled, with the exception of the exhaust hose and its attachment plate.

Despite the need for some degree of assembly, exclusive of the xTool M1, the parts are usually well-made and well-packaged, with adequate foam insulation to ensure safe transit and delivery. Fortunately, the rail, on which the laser will be mounted, is partially assembled, saving some time and labor, and ensuring that a critical component is factory-aligned.

The amount of time required for assembly varies with the user, with the range running from less than an hour to up to three hours. Care must be taken to ensure that the directions are followed precisely, and that every screw is tight, each belt is properly tensioned, and every cable is securely fitted.

All of the laser engravers have assembly manuals, although their on-line assembly videos are generally easier to follow, and have more detailed instructions. The D1 is somewhat easier to assemble since the electronics are already attached and the belts are in place. The M1 is virtually ready to use out of the box.

Of particular note, for those models requiring assembly, is taking care to make sure that the frame assembly is perfectly square. This is important because the movement of the laser head is dependent on its accurate movements to precise X- and Y-axis coordinates, in order to create an image, or form a cut. An out-of-square laser engraver will produce circles that are elliptical, and squares that are rectangular, among other anomalies.

Construction

The components that comprise the laser engraver can vary considerably from one manufacturer to another. The quality of the individual parts will impact both the performance of the device and its ultimate length of service.

The xTool D1 and M1, and the Ortur Laser Master 2 Pro, are solid, well-constructed devices.

The Ortur frame is made from powder-coated high-strength extruded T-slot aluminum. This frame material is readily available from a number of suppliers and can be used by the end-user to expand the size of the engraver footprint, although both Ortur and xTool sell extension kits. If the user modifies the device, exclusive of the manufacturer, he or she not only voids the warranty, but exposes him or herself to potential compatibility problems. Nonetheless some users have done so successfully.

The xTool D1 frame is custom-engineered with precision-fit components. The modern, sleek design of the frame partially conceals the electronics and the timing belts from the smoke and airborne debris generated by the laser. The Ortur design leaves the belts exposed on their top surfaces.

The xTool M1 is entirely self-enclosed, with all working components built into a strong plastic case. All further descriptions will exclude the M1, which is fully described in its own chapter.

The wheels on the Ortur that glide the laser head along its engraving or cutting path are made of D Type POM Polyoxymethylene, which is a hard, low-friction synthetic polymer plastic. The wheels on the D1 are made of industrial-grade steel, and are designed to fit precisely in the steel shafts that they glide upon. xTool claims that their all steel wheels last three times longer than plastic wheels. The D1 X-axis gantry has linear rods embedded into its surface to accurately guide the laser head movements with an accuracy up to 0.01mm.

Out-of-the-box the D1 is higher off the laser bed surface than the Ortur. This is beneficial for two reasons. First, it allows for a workpiece to be processed that is larger than the work surface, with the exception of the allowance of the small WiFi antenna on the front right that protrudes downward. A larger workpiece can slide in from either side, or from bottom to top, without raising the engraver frame. Second, the D1 can be raised upward using optional screw-in leg extenders, accommodating still thicker workpieces. The Ortur has optional third-party riser solutions as well as user-devised options.

Physical Size

The Ortur (400mm wide x 400mm deep, 15.75" x 15.75") and xTool (432mm x 406mm, 17" x 16") devices are very similar in size. Their engraving/cutting areas are sufficiently large for accomplishing most operations efficiently.

Potential buyers should be aware of the difference between a device's footprint, which is the amount of space it takes up on a work surface, and the machine's travel area, which is the maximum work space in which the device can operate.

Weight

Both the Ortur (3.8kg, 8.38 lb.) and the D1 (5kg, 11.02 lb.) are relatively light-weight, and, all things considered, can be lifted and moved by one person.

Laser Power

As has been mentioned elsewhere in this book, great care must be taken in assessing the rated power of a laser engraver/cutter. Generally speaking, a laser loses a significant amount of its power before it reaches the surface of a workpiece, due to heat loss. A good example of that is the 20W Ortur Laser Master 2 Pro,* which has an actual laser power of between 4.5-5.5W of output. The xTool D1, on the other hand, is advertised as a 10W laser engraver/cutter, and that is its actual output power. It constructs its 10W from two 5W lasers, in a unique proprietary configuration (FIG. 1). According to xTool, "The power of 10W dual laser xTool D1 is equivalent to a single laser 15W laser cutting machine."

The test of a laser is how thick a piece of wood it can cut in a single pass. The xTool D1 can cut a 10mm piece of wood at 100% power, 2% speed, in a single pass. The Ortur Laser Master 2 Pro is rated to cut a 9mm piece of wood at 100%, 100mm/min, in two passes.

Dot Size

The laser dot size, just as in assessing a laser printer, is a critical measure of the amount of detail that can be expressed. The smaller the dot size, the more dots per inch, the higher the definition of a photograph, the smoother the edges of shapes, the greater the clarity of small type. The dot size at optimal focus for the Ortur is 0.08 x 0.15mm. The xTool D1 dot size is 0.08 x 0.08mm.

Laser Shield

Around the base of the laser is an orange plexiglass shield that helps to contain the strong light emanating from the laser. Its purpose is to protect the operator's eyes, and those of anyone else in the immediate area. The Ortur shield is removeable, the xTool shield is not. Although shielding is important, is does not replace the need for adequate eye protection in the form of safety goggles.

Maintenance

xTool rates the expected life of its 10W laser at between 8000 and

Ortur sells two Laser Master 2 Pro models: one is optimized for engraving, one is optimized for cutting. A third model, the Laser Master 3, was introduced in June, 2022.

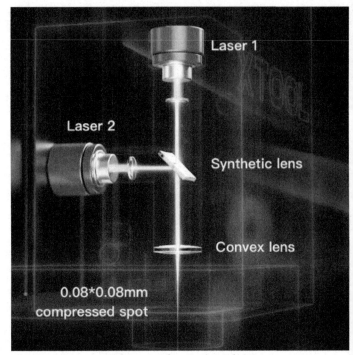

FIG. 1, The two 5W lasers in the xTool D1 laser engraver/cutter provide more engraving/cutting power than the Ortur Laser Master 2 Pro. Credit: xTool.

10,000 hours of use, which is fairly typical industry-wide. The life of the laser can be extended by avoiding running the laser at 100% power, and avoiding prolonged working sessions at high power.

A dirty light shield is indicative of a dirty lens. The user may also notice some degradation in engraving clarity or cutting accuracy. Optimum performance is dependent upon keeping the laser lens and the light shield clean. This is accomplished by turning the device power off, and removing the laser head. 91% Isopropyl alcohol should be applied on a lint-free cloth or paper towel to clean the light shield; a cotton swab soaked in alcohol should be used to clean the exposed laser surfaces. A helpful video published by xTool can be viewed here: https://youtu.be/lh53_cg6tW0

xTool suggests lubricating the steel shafts that the wheels run on to reduce friction and prevent rust. And, of course, maintain proper tension belt adjustments.

Proprietary Software

Ortur uses software available from third-parties, principally Light-Burn and LaserGRBL. LightBurn is compatible with Mac, Windows, and Linux, while LaserGRBL is Windows only. xTool, which can also be controlled with LightBurn, also has its own proprietary software called Laserbox Basic. Laserbox Basic, compatible with Mac and Windows, is bundled with the D1, and is designed as a simple program that can get a user producing simple designs quickly and easily. One of its main advantages is that it is designed specifically for the D1, so material settings are programmed in, freeing the user from the time-consuming process of running test target trials.

Materials

A wide range of materials can be processed on a diode laser engraver/

cutter, such as the Ortur Laser Master 2 Pro and xTool D1. These include paper, cardboard, wood, metal, leather, glass, fabric, bamboo, acrylic, plastic, ceramic, and even food.

Material Testing

The main challenge in laser engraving and cutting is determining the correct speed and power settings for a particular job, using a specific material. If there is no available material documentation, the user can either make an educated guess at settings, or run a test target using a piece of the actual material. After processing, the user needs to interpret the test results to determine the setting or settings that produce the best result(s).

Both Ortur and xTool provide guides that indicate the materials that they have tested and their optimum machine settings. Ortur's guide is general in nature, listing common categories, rather than specific materials (FIG. 2). It comes with the following warning: "The results would be different in even same material with different finishing or different colors. So you need to adjust the speed and power rate based on different objects."

xTool, on the other hand, has tested a wide range of materials, which they also sell directly to their users, with the specific machine settings provided (FIG. 3. Since the user is buying the same material that xTool has already tested to its satisfaction, the suggested settings will produce predictable, reliable results (FIG. 4).

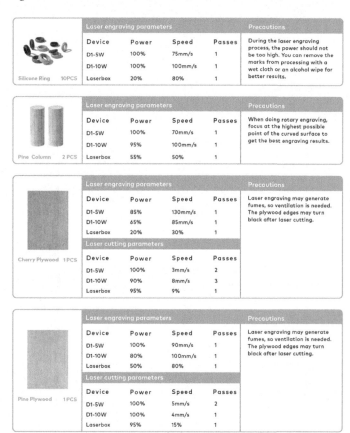

Laser engraving

Device parameters	Speed	Power	Processing time
Laserbox	50%	15%	1
D1 10W	50mm/s	30%	1
D1 5W	100mm/s	50%	1

FIG. 3. xTool has tested each of the materials they sell on their website. Here are the settings for engraving slate coasters using three of their laser engraver models. The Laserbox is their CO2 model. Credit: xTool

FIG. 4. A portion of the sheet with laser engraving and cutting settings that is provided with one of the xTool material boxes. Credit: xTool

	Ortur Laser Master 2 S2	Ortur Laser Master 2pro S2
Basswood Plywood	10000mm/min,M4,S500 10Lines/mm	10000mm/min,M4,S500 10Lines/mm
Pine Board	3000mm/min,M4,S200 20Lines/mm	10000mm/min,M4,S50 10Lines/mm
Paulownia Board	3000mm/min,M4,S200 10Lines/mm	5000mm/min,M4,S250 10Lines/mm
Gray Cardboard	3000mm/min,M4,S200 15Lines/mm	10000mm/min,M4,S50 15Lines/mm
White Cardboard	10000mm/min,M4,S1000 10Lines/mm	10000mm/min,M4,S1000 10Lines/mm
Corrugated Board	10000mm/min,M4,S500 10Lines/mm	10000mm/min,M4,S50 10Lines/mm
Black Acrylic	10000mm/min,M4,S500 15Lines/mm	10000mm/min,M4,S500 15Lines/mm
Acrylonitrile-Butadiene-Styrene	10000mm/min,M4,S1000 15Lines/mm	10000mm/min,M4,S1000 15Lines/mm
Epoxy Board	3000mm/min,M4,S200 15Lines/mm	10000mm/min,M4,S500 15Lines/mm
PolyVinyl Chloride	5000mm/min,M4,S250 10Lines/mm	5000mm/min,M4,S250 10Lines/mm
Leather	10000mm/min,M4,S500 10Lines/mm	10000mm/min,M4,S500 10Lines/mm
Cork Coaster	3000mm/min,M4,S250 10Lines/mm	5000mm/min,M4,S250 10Lines/mm

FIG. 2. A portion of the materials reference guide provided by Ortur. Credit: Ortur.

Workpiece Movement

It is very important that a workpiece remains stationary while undergoing laser processing. This is obvious since any movement will cause the laser to direct its beam where it should not be, potentially ruining the piece.

Even slight air movement on a piece of paper can cause it to move; the rush of air from an air assist can move a piece of light-weight wood; and the vibration of the moving laser head can shift the position of a piece of fabric or leather. In addition, warped wood will not lie flat and may catch on the laser head. For all of these reasons, and more, it may become necessary to secure a workpiece to the laser bed.

Common solutions are green painter's tape (stronger adhesive strength than blue), double-sided tape, small shallow metal weights, pegs that fit in the honeycomb openings, and, if the laser bed is metal, magnets.

Connection Options

In general, a laser engraver/cutter is driven by a computer, Mac or Windows, connected by a USB cable. There are, however, exceptions. First, is the optional Ortur off-line controller, an optional extra-cost device that can accept an SD card with instructions written in G-code, generated on a computer using a program such as LightBurn (FIG. 5). Second, is the built-in SD card reader on the xTool D1, that can also accept a job written on a computer in G-code.

The xTool D1 also has the options of using WiFi and an iPhone/Android app. Freedom from the USB cable means that the laser engraver can be operated at a distance apart from a desktop computer.

FIG. 5. The Ortur off-line controller will accept an SD card with a job written in G-code that has been generated on a computer. Credit: Ortur

Positioning

The Ortur Laser Master 2 Pro has mechanical limit switches that return the laser to the 0,0 X/Y coordinate position, which it identifies as Home. Options in LightBurn can be set to send the laser head to Home, move to the center or any significant location on the image, and also to frame the outline of an image.

xTool homes the laser to the left/back corner position. The user manually moves the laser head to the start position using the visible red laser-pointer cross-hairs, which are offset from the laser light itself. During operation the laser moves to where the cross hairs were positioned. The cross hairs, which can also frame an image, only serve to indicate a position, and are not bright enough to require safety glasses.

Belt Tension Adjustments

Proper belt tension is required to ensure that the laser head is always located at the precise coordinate locations specified by the software instructions. If it is not, images will be misshapen, output measurements will be incorrect, and in extreme cases, jobs will be grossly perverted.

During the assembly of the Ortur Laser Master 2 Pro, users are advised to leave sufficient slack in the belt so that it can stretched when it needs tightening. The ends of the belt are held in place with a washer and screw. Tightening requires removing the washer and screw, pulling on the belt, and re-securing it. Third-party suppliers have developed tensioners for more easily adjusting the Y-axis (FIG. 6).

FIG. 6. The Y-axis Tensioner for the Ortur Laser Master 2 Pro enables the user to adjust tension on the belts without removing the locking screw. Credit: KingGubby.com

xTool is the first company to use closed belts, which makes tensioning easier. xTool has screws that adjust tension on the two Y axis belts and one X axis belt using an ordinary Allen wrench.

Noise

The Ortur is fairly quiet, even when the laser is moving. The most likely source of noise is from an air assist, and in that case is dependent on the chosen air pump, which can be quite loud. xTool has a powerful fan that works to keep the laser head cool. Although it makes noise, it does so for a critically important reason. The optional xTool air assist set includes an air pump with little vibration and almost no noise.

Focus

Accurately setting the focus on the surface of a workpiece is essential to producing acceptable results, with sharp, crisp images, or clean, precise cuts. Both the Ortur Laser Master 2 Pro and the xTool D1 are fixed focus devices, meaning that they are factory-set to be in focus when they are set to a predetermined distance from their targets.

The Ortur uses a precision metal cylinder measuring 55mm, which is conveniently stored in a holder at the front of the machine. During focusing the cylinder is positioned between the bottom of the laser heat sink and the top of the workpiece. When the cylinder is snugly between them, the laser is in focus.

The D1 laser head incorporates a built-in ranging rod, which is swiveled out and down from the side of the laser head. When the laser is adjusted so that the rod is touching the top of the workpiece, the laser is in focus. The rod, which is held in place magnetically, is then returned to its upright storage position.

Focusing is accomplished by loosening the screw that holds the laser head in position, moving the laser up or down, and then tightening the screw to lock the setting in place.

The space between the top of a workpiece and the bottom of the laser is measured in the Z dimension. This Z-axis setting is, obviously, a critical setting, but is limited to the built-in adjustment range of the laser. It can, of course, be increased simply by raising the frame of the laser engraver up to increase the distance.

In order to easily accommodate thicker workpieces, yet keep the laser engraver at its factory set height, the user can buy a Z-height adjuster that increases the range in which the Z-height can be extended. A number of third-party Z-height adjusters are available for the Ortur Laser Master 2 Pro (FIG. 7) and the D1.

FIG. 7. This Z-axis adjuster replaces the one that came with the Ortur Laser Master 2 Pro, providing 40mm of travel. Credit: KingGubby.com

Air Assist

An essential element in the use of a laser, especially for cutting, is air assist (FIG. 8). This is clearly stated elsewhere in this book. Its benefit is also clearly evident in the fact that neither the Ortur nor the xTool D1 were originally sold with air assist, yet both now offer it as an add-on. In addition to its availability directly from both companies, various air assist solutions are available from a variety of third-party suppliers.

FIG. 8. The xTool air assist add-on provides a consistent flow of high-pressure air to move smoke away from a workpiece surface, thus avoiding yellowing, soot, and other forms of discoloration. The metal nozzle resists high temperatures, and the air pump is both powerful and quiet. Credit: xTool

Laser Bed

The standard design of both the Ortur and the xTool D1 laser engravers is an open laser bed. Either device can be used on any flat, nonflammable surface. However, that surface will be susceptible to the intense heat of the laser, and will ultimately be burned, scorched, and discolored. Users typically place their laser frame over a piece of plywood, MDF, or similar solid, smooth material, which becomes, in essence, a spoil-board; a surface that will show the abuse of repeated burns. One advantage of using a material that is susceptible to burning is that the user can purposefully engrave a grid on the spoil-board that can serve to position and align a workpiece or a jig. Grid configuration files are readily available on-line.

An important consideration in the selection of the laser bed surface is its appropriateness for laser cutting. Laser cuts are best performed when there is space below the areas to be cut, in order to allow for the movement of air. That solution, typically found on expensive CO_2 laser cutters, is the use of a metal honeycomb base (FIG. 9). Users have improvised suitable honeycomb bases, and xTool sells a honeycomb working panel set made specifically for the model D1.

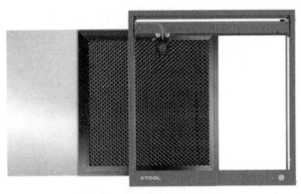

FIG. 9. *The xTool Honeycomb Working Panel Set consists of an aluminum base that fits beneath a precision iron honeycomb panel. The set, which can be used with any right-sized laser engraver, helps to exhaust smoke and keep the back of materials, such as wood, clean. Credit: xTool*

Enclosure

A laser engraver presents a number of potential dangers to its immediate working environment. Among them are the intensity of the light emitted by the laser, and the smoke, fumes, and odors emitted by the interaction of the laser beam and a workpiece. As a health precaution, users can surround the laser engraver/cutter with an enclosure. The enclosure shields the operator from these potential hazards, as well as reduces the possibility of the spread of fire.

One consideration in adding an enclosure is the use of a rotary device, for imaging cylindrical objects. The rotary requires that the laser engraver frame be lifted to allow for the height of the cylindrical item to be engraved. This height typically exceeds the space provided in the enclosure. For this reason, if an enclosure is used, it is not secured to the laser engraver base so that the engraver and the enclosure can be lifted independently.

Enclosures are available from a variety of sources, including the original equipment manufacturers.. Many users have resorted to building their own, since a vendor-supplied enclosure can rival the cost of the laser engraver itself. Also available are generic enclosure designs that can fit a variety of different laser engraver/cutters (FIG. 10).

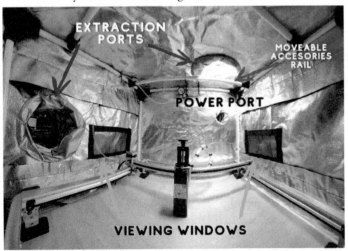

FIG. 10. *The King Gubby Laser Enclosure Tent with Smoke Extraction is a lower-cost alternative to OEM solutions. It is compatible with a wide selection of laser frames and offers add-ons for an exhaust fan, lighting, camera mounts, heat alarm, and viewing window. Credit: kinggubby.com*

Camera

LightBurn software supports the use of a high-resolution USB digital camera, positioned over the laser bed, and capturing a clear image of the workpiece(s) to be processed. The purpose of the camera is threefold: to accurately position work on the laser bed; to trace simple artwork from the camera image; and to monitor the operation of the laser (FIG. 11). The camera cable is connected to the computer, not to the laser engraver.

FIG. 11. *The use of a camera makes it possible to scan an image directly from the laser bed, trace it, and then move the tracing over a workpiece with precision placement. Photo credit: LightBurn.*

Any laser engraver that uses LightBurn can benefit from the use of a camera. If the laser engraver is mounted inside an enclosure, then the camera is mounted directly above the center of the laser bed, on the inside of the top of the enclosure. If the laser engraver is not mounted inside an enclosure, the user can buy a third-party camera mount, available on Etsy. In either case, the user should check the LightBurn website to determine supported camera models.

Not all lasers natively support the use of a camera, therefore many third-party providers have created 3D-printed rigs to attach to a number of popular laser engravers. These devices can usually be found on Etsy. The cameras themselves can be purchased directly from the publishers of the LightBurn software. The camera is operated by opening the Camera Control window in LightBurn.

Regardless of how the camera is mounted, it must be carefully focused, showing as much of the laser bed as possible, and securely mounted away from the laser head path. In addition, the camera must have adequate lighting in order to capture sharp, clear images. LightBurn provides a detailed description of the calibration and alignment process at https://lightburnsoftware.github.io/NewDocs/UsingACamera.html.

Control Language

The standard language for CNC (Computer Numerical Control) machines, of which a laser engraver/cutter is one, is G-code. All of the engraving and cutting devices, and their control software, described in this book, use G-code.

User Community Support

In this age of social media there is a strong, thriving community of laser engraver/cutting users. There is help available in the form of users' groups, forums, FAQs, vendor discussion groups, YouTube videos, etc. for those considering a purchase, those new to the craft, those finding new uses and applications, those opening businesses and exploring for-profit opportunities, those wanting to share what they have learned, and those just curious what all the excitement is about.

Safety

Both the Ortur Laser Master 2 Pro and the xTool D1 have built-in safety features that can work to avoid mishaps. Both devices will stop if the laser is bumped, or an object moves into its path. Both devices have an emergency stop button, will shut off if the laser remains in one spot for too long, and will shut down if the USB connection, or WiFi in the case of the D1, is interrupted.

Rotary

The rotary attachment takes the place of the Y-axis, turning a cylindrical object, such as a drinking cup, or water bottle, so that the laser engraver can be focused on its turning surface. The Ortur rotary requires assembly, and the user must physically disconnect the default Y-axis cable, and plug in the rotary cable. The xTool D1 rotary comes completely assembled, and plugs directly into a port on the controller board (FIG. 12).

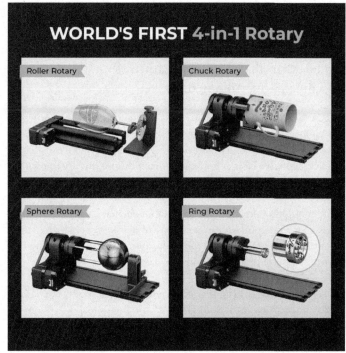

FIG. 13. *The xTool RA2 Pro rotary is the world's most flexible device for imaging cylindrical and spherical objects. Credit: xTool*

FIG. 12. *A rotary attachment (Ortur on the left, xTool on the right) enables a user to engrave on cylindrical objects. Credits: Ortur, xTool*

In April, 2022, xTool released the xTool RA2 Pro rotary, billed as the world's first 4-in-1 rotary, capable of engraving irregular cylindrical and spherical objects, from mugs to rings (FIG. 13). The 4-in-1 rotary includes an assortment of fittings to accommodate the shapes of a wide variety of irregularly shaped objects using precise, adjustable jaws to securely hold articles in place. The versatile kit includes cables for use with AtomStack, Ortur, Twotrees, and NEJE laser engravers.

Warranty

Ortur offers a full one-year warranty, with free repairs. xTool's warranty varies from six months to one year depending on the particular part in question, with free repairs or replacement. Both company warranties are subject to the terms listed on their websites.

17. Lessons in Laser Engraving

It has been almost a year since I began my self-education into laser engraving and cutting, which led to publishing this book. In that time, I've learned many things, some of which may not be obvious from what you've read in the preceding pages. Among them are:

• There is a cachet surrounding laser engraving, evoking futuristic and high-tech images from Star Wars and James Bond movies. You, like me, are likely the first and only person in your family or neighborhood to own a laser engraver. There is a certain novelty to owning this new category of tool, and being able to master it.

• Not enough is said about the smells that emanate from various materials that undergo laser processing. Rubber is probably the worst, but even wood, probably the most common material, leaves an odor that can be quite obnoxious and long-lasting.

• Laser engraving/cutting is a fairly new choice for hobbyists. There is still much to be learned in terms of the pre- and post-treatment of materials. There's still a lot of room for experimentation and discovery.

• New users often give up too soon and too easily. Learning to use a laser engraver is not a particularly difficult skill, although doing it consistently well does take practice and patience. In time, anyone applying a reasonable degree of determination can master it.

• Producing certain types of work, such as photographic images on canvas, can take hours of processing time. Many users seem to undervalue their effort. If the work is to be sold, the user should place a fair and realistic value on what their time is worth.

• A realistic view of the limitations of a given laser engraver/cutter is just as important as a realistic understanding of its capabilities.

• The laser engraver/cutter is only as capable as the software that drives it. An investment in third-party software (i.e. LightBurn) should be seriously considered.

• Engraving on a one-of-a-kind, or expensive item is risky. If a trial burn can be done on the backside, or a facsimile piece of scrap, do so. If not, reconsider doing it at all.

• Before pressing the start button: Did you set the focus? Did you check the power/speed settings? Did you place and position the material properly? Do you have the time to complete the job? Is your environment safe?

• The laser engraving field is evolutionary, with innovations constantly coming to market. Machine capabilities will mature; with faster, more powerful lasers, and new workflow productivity improvements.

• Laser engraving machines mate nicely with 3D printers. Users with 3D printers can manufacture a growing number of accessories that enhance the use of the engraver.

• Laser engravers are shipped with firmware that is, of course, current at the time of manufacture. It is likely that the firmware will need to be updated to correct bugs or to implement new features. Users should remain in contact with the manufacturer to learn of updates, improvements, and new accessories.

• Developing the skill to troubleshoot processing problems is just as important as developing the skill to produce well-crafted work.

• A laser engraver/cutter is made with an enormous amount of potential creative power. It can be used to produce an extraordinarily large variety of things, all waiting to be released, like a genie in a bottle.

• I've been using Hallmark Card Studio software for years. It provides instant access to just about any kind of social expression card, which I can personalize; or I can create a totally unique card from scratch. With index stock for the card, my color printer, and matching envelopes, I can have a greeting card ready to go in as little as 5 minutes. No driving to the store to shop for a card, no leaving the house. So too can it be with a laser engraver/cutter. Personalized gifts can be made for virtually any occasion, and rather quickly. Case in point, a canasta partner was celebrating his birthday. I made him a card and custom box for storing four decks of canasta cards. My own gift shop!

• After spending time researching and writing the chapter on Stencils, I was surprised to see a font that is essentially the opposite of a stencil. Some of the signs at Five Below, a national retailer selling items from one to five dollars, feature a font with the counter spaces completely filled in.

• Diode laser engraver/cutters are a fairly new phenomenon. Most of the FaceBook groups related to the technology have been formed fairly recently. The concurrent spread of COVID-19, and the need to restrict human interaction and movement outside the home, has likely been a big contributor to the popularity of laser engraving. Laser engravers can be purchased easily, and relatively inexpensively, online; can be assembled and operated by a single person in a minimum amount of space, and can result in releasing pent-up human energy and creative expression.

• Another reason for the growth of laser engraving is the prevalence of personal computers. Everyone has one; and since it is a vital part of a laser engraving/cutting workflow, users have already made that part of the financial commitment, and probably have the essential skills necessary to deal with the operating system, install and navigate new software, and potentially master the challenges of learning new software applications.

• Other than those who use their laser engraver for a business, most users produce things for friends and family…for gifts and keepsakes. They use it as a tool for ornamentation of something that exists, like a watch band, or for personalization of something that is a totally new creation, like an award.

• Dongguan Ortur intelligent Technologies Co., Ltd. released the results of a Laser Engraving Survey on June 16, 2022. Among their findings are:

—the exposed linear rail design of laser engravers introduces safety hazards, and exposes the environment to dust.

—diode laser engravers are too slow to be used in commercial operations.

—users rate as "Very Good" available software as meeting their expectations.

—there needs to be an industry standard for laser module power ratings.

—what laser engraver users want most is stronger laser modules and faster engraving speeds.

—protective enclosures, with key locks to prevent accidental child use, should become the norm.

—laser engravers should incorporate more capable rotary attachments, auto focusing, honeycomb waste boards, safety enclosures, and air filtration.

—customer response times need to be reduced, spare parts need to be more accessible, instruction manuals need better descriptions and explanations, tutorials need to be more plentiful and in-depth, and manufacturers need to offer a wider variety of engravable materials.

—of the 991 survey respondents, 94% are male; 88% own their own engraving machine; 94% have three or less years of experience with the technology; and 26% are using their machines for commercial purposes.

The survey results were posted on the Official Ortur User FaceBook Group page.

• A very specialized form of laser engraving is 3D Engraving on Wood or Acrylic, which creates a three-dimensional relief image. The process, which has been demonstrated using CO2 lasers, requires considerable file preparation and post finishing. The process begins with a vector file that is converted into grayscale. The darkest black areas equal the deepest engraving, the whitest white areas equal no engraving, and shades in between use a power and speed proportional to grayscale values. The process can be viewed in a YouTube video from Trotec entitled "3D Wooden Engraving | Laser Engrave 3D Coat of Arms." In time, this process is likely to become doable on diode laser engravers.

Credit: Trotec

• In the realm of laser engraver/cutters there are three major categories: Diode Laser, CO2, and Fiber. This book has only dealt with diode lasers.

The diode laser is the least expensive, and can operate in a relatively large workspace since they can be moved, or can, using LightBurn, divide a large job into smaller units. Most units are small enough to be considered desktop laser units.

CO2 lasers can be purchased at prices ranging from the higher-end of the diode lasers, to the tens of thousands of dollars. Unlike diode lasers, they require a cooling unit, and are always sold in a secure metal enclosure. CO2 lasers are considerably more powerful than diode lasers. In addition to the industrial models from Epilog, Trotec, Monport, and others, there are consumer/hobbyist models from Glowforge, Muse, and Dremel.

Fiber lasers, so named because they use optical fiber cable to transmit light, mainly engrave and cut metal very quickly, and have prices that start at about $3000. They have a small work area, as little as 6" square, which can be expanded by using a different lens, or a more powerful laser. Unlike diode and CO2 lasers which use a gantry that moves the laser head along X and Y coordinates, the fiber laser head is fixed. The laser head uses a galvo mechanism consisting of a set of mirrors that reflect the laser light and project it through a fixed lens. Neither a cooling unit nor air assist are required, although an exhaust system is necessary to remove smoke and fumes.

Just to complicate things, CO2 lasers can also incorporate a galvo head, meaning that instead of directing the laser across the work surface using X and Y axes, it moves the laser by directing it with fast-moving mirrors.

• The rapid development of technical advancements, improvements, and innovations is not likely to stop. In June, 2022 both Ortur and xTool released models with significant new features.

The Ortur Laser Master 3 10W

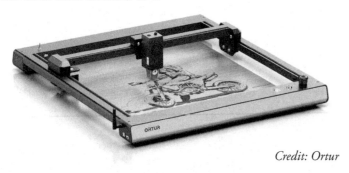

Credit: Ortur

In the summer of 2022, Ortur announced the global launch of the Ortur Laser Master 3 (LM3), its third-generation laser engraver/cutter.

The open frame design of the LM3 is sleeker than its predecessors, with its belts hidden under its aluminum body, protecting them from ambient dust, dirt, and air-borne contaminants. The machine is distinct in two major regards: its speed and its power. The engraving speed is rated at 20000mm/min, making it twice as fast as the Laser Master 2 Pro, and most of its competitors. The diode laser is rated at a true 10W, composed of the power of two 5.5W lasers concentrated through a set of lenses, producing a spot size of 0.05 x 0.1mm.

The engineering team devoted special attention to making this model one of the safest on the market, with seven distinct safety features. The first, and most obvious is the requirement for a key, to be able to operate the machine. This feature is particularly important in environments where children are present, or situations where there are

concerns about tampering or unsupervised use. The prominent red Emergency Stop Button remains at the front of the machine, which stops operation when pressed, and is twisted to unlock.

A true innovation is the integration of an air assist interface in the laser module. This makes the use of an external air compressor of at least 40ml/min, much easier to attach and use since the laser nozzle has the air outlet pre-installed. Also built into the laser head is the focal gauge, a drop-down lever used for focusing.

The recommended software applications continue to be LightBurn and LaserGRBL, although Ortur provides Laser Explorer, an app for iPhone, Android, iPads, and Android devices. The app provides a quick and easy way to print photos directly from a wireless connected device.

The xTool D1 Pro 20W

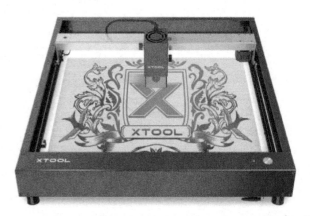

Credit: xTool

In June of 2022 xTool announced the world's most powerful diode laser yet, the xTool D1 Pro, available with either a 5W, 10W, or 20W laser head. The top-of-the-line device features a true 20W laser, composed of four 5W lasers combined in a single module. The module includes the ranging rod for focusing, with a unique mechanism that simplifies the calculation of the target depth for cutting, which they recommend to be one-half the thickness of the material. Also part of the module is a built-in air assist nozzle, an improved Z-axis locking knob, and a flame detector. The powerful laser can cut 10mm basswood, or 8mm black acrylic in a single pass. The device uses improved algorithms and a processing speed up to 400mm/s (24000mm/min), which can result in a productivity increase of up to 65%.

The built-in air assist nozzle greatly simplifies the process of implementing the air assist capability by simply requiring the addition of an adequate air compressor.

Also new are built-in limit switches that automatically sense boundaries in all four directions, eliminating annoying laser head frame collisions. Should the laser head approach a limit switch it will stop and an alarm will sound.

The machine, available in either a golden red or metal gray finish, supports the extension kit and all of the D1 accessories.

The following pages are available as
a protected PDF with live links.

The password is the first word in the first paragraph of Chapter 12.

https://www.dropbox.com/s/zpu894dcyb15nb8/Focusing%20on%20Engraving%20Appendices.pdf?dl=0

Look for news about Laser Engraving at *http://kleperreport.com*

Focusing on Laser Engraving and Decorating

Affordable, Versatile, and Creative Marking, Engraving, and Cutting

Available on Amazon.com

International Standard Book Number: 9 780930 904074

Selected Bibliography

Acrylic

How to Paint Engraved Acrylic
https://youtu.be/3LEWBSZER1g

Engraving Acrylic
https://laserweb.yurl.ch/videos/49-engraving-acrylic

Etching on Acrylic
https://youtu.be/2s9q6tl7SRc

Types of Acrylic
https://nbm.uberflip.com/i/1431218-december-21/48?

Adding Color

Engraving with Color
https://www.youtube.com/watch?v=ea-exuB32ZI

Coloring Metal with Alcohol Inks
https://www.limabeads.com/Coloring-Metal-with-Alcohol-Inks-T37

Adding Color How to color fill laser engraved wood sign
https://youtu.be/hDPYWFByGCg

Tile etch paints
https://www.facebook.com/groups/522775308373490/learning_content/?filter=814420675845838&post=190777536514900

Air Assist

Why Air Assist is Essential to your laser engraver
https://omtechlaser.com/blogs/why-air-assist-is-essential-to-your-laser.engraver/resource-hub

Air Assist Air Assist for Beginners
https://makerfreedom.com/air-assist-for-beginners-laser-cutting/

Air Assist Air Assist A Laser Operator's Best Friend
http://blog.fslaser.com/experts/air-assist-a-laser-operators-best-friend
Air Assist

Air Assist to Reduce Flare-Ups
https://www.epiloglaser.com/laser-machines/fusion-laser/fusion-air-assist.htm

Air compressor for laser cutter/ engraver
https://www.artesea.ch/playground/workshop/laser/air-compressor-laser-cutter.engraver

Laser Air Assist Shootout
https://hackaday.io/project/179362-laser-air-assist-shootout

The Laser Wizard
https://www.youtube.com/watch?v=6Ie2bCYlITQ

Color Fill

Color Filling Techniques for engraving and carving
https://www.youtube.com/watch?v=9WNd82-K09E

Tip for coloring engraving
https://youtu.be/fFwXT2XgQKs

Cutting

How to Get Started With Laser Cutting? – Beginners Guide
https://makerdesignlab.com/tutorials-tips/laser-cutting-beginners-guide/

Online File Generators for Laser Cutting
https://makerdesignlab.com/tutorials-tips/online-file-generators-for-laser-cutting/

Cutting Laser Cutter
https://www.productdesigny.com/media/viewer/digital_fabrication_laser_cutter

Diode

All you need to know about diode lasers and laser diodes
https://www.manufacturingtomorrow.com/story/2020/02/all-you-need-to-know.about-diode-lasers-and-laser-diodes/14731/

DXF

What Is a DXF File? How to open, edit, and convert DXF files
https://www.lifewire.com/dxf-file-4138558

DXF Files
https://www.adobe.com/creativecloud/file-types/image/vector/dxf-file.html

Enclosures

Ortur Enclosure Review: specifications, price, features
https://www.priceboon.com/product/ortur-enclosure/

Engraver

Introduction-to-laser-engraving/ 10 Tips For Laser Engraving And Cutting
https://yorahome.com/pages/10-tips-for-laser-engraving-and-cutting

Etch

Marking metal with a cheap laser and mustard |different types of mustard tested
https://www.youtube.com/watch?v=hEQG6NxPke8

Focus

Ortur Laser -Achieving the Ultimate Focus!
https://youtu.be/dHAgp1HoZkw

Appendices

Focusing a Diode Laser Quickly - Featuring the Ortur Laser Master 2
https://youtu.be/ghkwMgtAU5A

Laser focusing on Laser Master 2 Pro and optimal line spacing - CNXSoftware
https://www.cnx-software.com/2021/07/11/laser-focusing-on-laser-master-2-pro.optimal-line-spacing/

How small can you make a diode laser spot? - Hardware - LightBurnSoftware Forum
https://forum.lightburnsoftware.com/t/how-small-can-you-make-a-diode-laser.spot/14731

G-Code

G-code Explained | List of Most Important G-code Commands
https://howtomechatronics.com/tutorials/g-code-explained-list-of-most-important.g-code-commands/

G-Code
https://en.wikipedia.org/wiki/G-code

GCode upload to SD-Card - LightBurn Software - LightBurn SoftwareForum
https://forum.lightburnsoftware.com/t/gcode-upload-to-sd-card/35254

LightBurn save-as G-code
https://makezine.com/2016/10/24/get-to-know-your-cnc-how-to-read-g-code/

What is G-code? - Definition from WhatIs.com
https://whatis.techtarget.com/definition/G-code

G-code List of G and M Codes Supported by Lightburn - LightBurn Software -LightBurn Software Forum
https://forum.lightburnsoftware.com/t/list-of-g-and-m-codes-supported-by.lightburn/11520

G-code G-Code Tutorial for CNC Programming: 6 Simple Steps | All3DP
https://all3dp.com/2/cnc-milling-programming-basic-cnc-g-code-tutorial/

Glass

Glass Engraving workshop
https://www.youtube.com/watch?v=f833oyuap88

Engraving glass
https://fb.watch/8IAb0fELcX/

Engraving Glass
https://support.thunderlaserusa.com/portal/en/kb/articles/best-practics-for-engraving-glass

History

The History & Basics of Laser Cutters
https://www.beautyandthebolt.com/blog/the-history-and-basics-of-laser-cutters

The Evolution and History of Laser Marking and Engraving
https://www.permanentmarking.com/history-of-laser-marking/

Imaging Base

Hacking The Ortur Laser With Spoil Board, Z-Height,
https://hackaday.com/2021/03/23/hacking-the-ortur-laser-with-spoil-board-z-

Imaging Base Laser Hack: Using Legos for a Template or Jig
https://www.youtube.com/watch?v=aYFvHWLnE3g

Kerf

What is cutting kerf?
https://www.esabna.com/us/en/education/blog/what-is-cutting-kerf.cfm

What is kerf in laser cutting?
https://sendcutsend.com/what-is-kerf-in-laser-cutting/

Kerf Figuring out kerf for precision parts
https://www.ponoko.com/blog/ponoko/figuring-out-kerf-for-precision-parts/

Kerf Cutting technique for bending applications
https://www.troteclaser.com/en-us/knowledge/tips-for-laser-users/bending.technique/

Kerf How to Adjust for Wood Thickness and Kerf on a Laser
https://www.instructables.com/How-to-Adjust-for-Wood-Thickness-and-Kerf-on.Cutter at Techshopa-Las/

Lasers

Finia Emblaser 2 Laser Cutter With Air Assist, Camera, And WiFi
https://www.micromark.com/Afinia-Emblaser-2-Laser-Cutter

RIT Image Permanence Institute
https://www.imagepermanenceinstitute.org

LightBurn

LightBurn settings
https://m.youtube.com/watch?fbclid=IwAR0ToRNSKgWbKnUJk8_n.i9UQq3YYcUtVZRuRdSU_UafIKeicP89_cq9tzk&v=nybhYtjElQU&feature=youtu. be Cut Settings Basics LightBurn

https://lightburnsoftware.github.io/NewDocs/CutSettingsWindow.html

LightBurn Home - LightBurn Software Documentation
https://lightburnsoftware.github.io/NewDocs/index.html

Marking

CerMark Black Laser MarkingTechnology for Metals
https://www.amazon.com/Spotted-Dog-LMM-6000-CerMark.Technology/dp/B079F2MQ4Q?tag=brancull-20&geniuslink=true

Material

Basswood
https://www.wood-database.com/basswood/

Basswood
https://en.wikipedia.org/wiki/Tilia_americana

Medium-density fibreboard
https://en.wikipedia.org/wiki/Medium-density_fibreboard

MDF 101
https://www.bobvila.com/articles/what-is-mdf/

Material Library
https://forum.lightburnsoftware.com/t/material-library-for-ortur-lm2-20w/29238

Slate
https://www.productdesigny.com/media/viewer/digital_fabrication__laser_cutter#Materials

Laser-cut decals out of duct tape
https://youtu.be/27MXU8wII-M

Laser Tips & Tricks using Blue Painter's Tape
https://www.youtube.com/watch?v=2UyKLNxEYgU

Types of Materials to Process with ULS Laser Systems
https://www.ulsinc.com/material/materials-library

Material Beilstein Test
https://youtu.be/GYVy7qE8kP4

Material Selection Guide: How to Choose a Proper Material for Laser Processing – Snapmaker
https://support.snapmaker.com/hc/en-us/articles/4409740554903-Material.Selection-Guide-How-to-Choose-a-Proper-Material-for-Laser-Processing

How to Choose the Best Wood for Laser Engraving - Laser Engraving Tips
https://laserengravingtips.com/how-to-choose-the-best-wood-for-laser-engraving/

Material Choosing the Best Wood for Laser Cutting or Engraving Project
https://www.thunderlaserusa.com/best-wood-for-laser-cutting-engraving-project/

Selecting the Perfect Wood for Laser Engraving
https://www.laserengravedmemories.com/en/laser-engraving-wood-how-to.html

Material Which are the best materials for laser engraving? - Laser Engraving Tips
https://laserengravingtips.com/which-are-the-best-materials-for-laser-engraving/

LASERCUT4 | Laser cutting of Bamboo and a variety of other materials
https://www.lasercut4.com/en/wood/bamboo

Smokey Hill Designs
https://smokeyhilldesigns.com/pages/contact-us

Laser Cutting Materials Guide
https://makerfreedom.com/laser-cutting-materials-guide/

Laser Etching Metal: Everything You Want to Know
https://dxtech.com/laser-etching-metal-everything-you-want-to-know/

Ortur

Ortur User Manual Laser Master 2
https://drive.google.com/file/d/1dwGRLfdtfbXW-3m2uvvv6wQwddM1B-gRD/view

Ortur Laser Master 2 Pro in practical test
https://basic-tutorials.com/ortur-laser-master-2-pro-in-practical-test/2/

Ortur Laser Master 2 Pro laser engraver - First impressions – CNX Software
https://www.cnx-software.com/2021/06/02/ortur-laser-master-2-pro-laser.engraver-first-impressions/

Hands On With The Ortur Laser Cutter | Hackaday
https://hackaday.com/2021/02/23/hands-on-with-the-ortur-laser-cutter/

Ortur Official GBAtemp Review: Ortur Laser Master 2 Pro and rotating stand (Hardware)
https://gbatemp.net/review/ortur-laser-master-2-pro-and-rotating-stand.1853/

We Tested the Ortur Laser Master 2 Pro (Review & Full Specs) -CNC Sourced
https://www.cncsourced.com/reviews/ortur-laser-master-2-pro-review-specs-test/

Ortur Laser Master 2 review | TechRadar
https://www.techradar.com/reviews/ortur-laser-master-2

Ortur Laser Master 2 Review: Big Laser, Little Power | All3DP
https://all3dp.com/1/ortur-laser-master-2-review-specs/ http://www.ortur3d.com/en/list2.htm

Ortur Ortur Offline Controller Install
https://youtu.be/srdAY9iJhEs

Rotary

How to Create and Etch a Custom design on a Tumbler. Ortur LM2
https://youtu.be/SbMdKmxErag

Rotary Assembly of the Rotary Attachment for the Ortur LM2 - 20W with Lightburn...
https://youtu.be/edft7-FNyDE

Ortur Manuals – Rotary
https://lasergrbl.com/ortur-manuals/

Software

Ortur Power Burn Test
https://drive.google.com/file/d/1lnNp8_OHRSMt_2rY5e77t6dNCyex-0u8h/view

Inkscape
https://inkscape.org

Software Slicer
https://www.imag-r.com/slicer

The Rasterbator
https://rasterbator.net

Appendices

Laser Cutter Software
https://lasergods.com/downloads/

LaserWeb software
https://laserweb.yurl.ch/

7 Best Laser Engraving & Cutter Software (Free & Paid!) -CNC Sourced
https://www.cncsourced.com/rankings/best-laser-cutter-engraving-software/

Graphic Tracer
https://www.graphicpowers.com/

RDWorks WIN
https://rdworks.software.informer.com/8.0/

Software Cutting Master 3 WIN
https://cutting-master-3.software.informer.com

PhotoGrav 3.1 | PhotoGrav
https://www.photograv.com/product/photograv-3-1/

Prepare image to laser engraving with photoshop.
https://youtu.be/H2ULldN28V8

Photo Editing Service for Laser Engraving – Laser Illusions Technology
https://www.laserillusionstech.com/product/digital-product-1/

Engraving Photoshop Action Graphics, Designs & Templates
https://graphicriver.net/engraving+photoshop+action-in-graphics

How I Prepare Photos for Engraving Using Photoshop
https://community.glowforge.com/t/how-i-prepare-photos-for-engraving-using-photoshop/41566

Stencils

Laser Cut Stencil Letters
https://www.instructables.com/Laser-Cut-Stencil-Letters/

Stencilano
https://subsidiarydesign.com/stencilano/

Stencils Online
https://www.stencilsonline.com/design-your-own/

iStencils
https://istencils.com

Beginner's Guide for Laser Cutting Stencils
https://jackforge.com/laser-cutting-stencils/

Sun Catcher Stencil Generator
https://suncatcherstudio.com/stencil-maker/

Surface Cleaning

Laser Hack: Cleaning Material with a Magic Eraser
https://www.youtube.com/watch?v=XwI7-OFcFmg

Surface Prep

How to... Wood engraving with BAKING SODA?
https://www.youtube.com/watch?v=af7u-2BjOMc

Rust-Oleum 7585838 Spray Paint, 20.Ounce, Cold, 20 Ounce
https://www.youtube.com/watch?v=LR9CDz8y_LA

LaserBond 100
https://www.laserbondingtech.com/shop

The Kenny Hack: The best pre-stain/treatment for lasers out there?
https://youtu.be/zsnldGA1U98

Laser Engraving With Borax
https://youtu.be/JaiIS_aKSDY

Etch glass with tempura
https://youtu.be/mZtpByeJpKo

Color paper
https://orturoffice.com/collections/accessories/products/ortur-laser-engraving.machine-tool-color-paper-to-color-miniature-glass-stone-material-crystal-jade.accessories?variant=40322418344112&fbclid=IwAR0nVx9r74OufqeTMAGHUkKSL0mKEG7NNmwc31UtBGmN7qMHY4b3gGoY2XA

Titanium Dioxide (TiO2)
http://blog.workshop88.com/2021/04/06/norton-white-tile-principal-component.method/?fbclid=IwAR3xU2HNf0ddOTMBGm_fuGF-Sa-7esrT2RD_-4zPWAMqHDyt59smBNamKuwqA

Cermark vs. Dry Moly Lube
https://youtu.be/5ziyB9EEnL8

Laser Foil
https://s3.amazonaws.com/jpmagento.public/documents/techtips/JPP_TechTips_LaserFoil.pdf

How to Make Steel Wool and Vinegar Stain (8 Ways) | Saws on Skates®
https://sawsonskates.com/steel-wool-and-vinegar-stain/

Power Scale for Baking Soda Testing | Lightburn File – Laser Illusions Technology | Custom Laser Engraving & Cutting
https://www.laserillusionstech.com/product/power-scale-for-baking-soda-testing.lightburn-file/

Airbrushing Norton White Tile Principal Component Method
http://blog.workshop88.com/2021/04/06/norton-white-tile-principal-component.method/

All you need to know about laser etching (marking, engraving)
https://endurancelasers.com/all-you-need-to-know-about-laser-marking/

How to Darken Laser Engraving on Wood
https://laserengravingtips.com/how-to-darken-laser-engraving-on-wood/

Wood

Laser Engraving and Cutting withCNC Lasers
https://optlasersgrav.com/wood-laser-engraving-and-cutting

How to remove the burn marks from engraving
https://www.youtube.com/watch?v=RSPbr9afObk

Laser Hack: Sanding Wood After Laser Engraving
https://www.youtube.com/watch?v=QSEKkVGz1N0

11 Wood Sanding Tips Tricks and Hacks to Save Time and Money
https://www.empireabrasives.com/blog/wood-sanding-tips-tricks-hacks

How to Seal Laser Engraved Wood: Detailed Guide - Maker Industry
https://makerindustry.com/how-to-seal-laser-engraved-wood/

How to Seal a Wood Sign + do you really need to? – Creative Ramblings
https://www.creativeramblingsblog.com/how-to-seal-a-wood-sign/

4 Ways to Seal Wood - wikiHow
https://www.wikihow.com/Seal-Wood

Surface Prep Woodworking FINISHES / Complete Guide
https://youtu.be/SWLm-3_iogw

How to Burn Designs Into Wood using your Cricut!
https://www.youtube.com/watch?v=eCTfk_90xVQ

Testing

Test Your Material to Determine Laser Speed and Power Settings
https://www.instructables.com/Test-your-material-to-determine-laser-speed-and-po/

Finding a material's best engraving settings
https://darklylabs.zendesk.com/hc/en-us/articles/115000351332-Finding-a-material-s-best-engraving-settings

Hole Gauge for Laser Cutter - STLFinder
https://www.stlfinder.com/model/hole-gauge-for-laser-cutter-v88JRw-ga/2758344/

Simplified Material Test Card - STLFinder
https://www.stlfinder.com/model/simplified-material-test-card.EZ-siLE7U/2459938/

Check out this amazing find from Etsy.com: File - Power scale -LightBurn
https://www.etsy.com/listing/1081870455/file-power-scale-lightburn

Testing Laser Cut Test File
https://www.etsy.com/listing/813282229/laser-cut-test-file

Testing Lightburn PowerScale Generators - O2 Creative
https://o2creative.co.nz/laser/

Test Your Material to Determine Laser Speed and Power Settings : 4Steps (with Pictures) - Instructables
https://www.instructables.com/Test-your-material-to-determine-laser-speed-and.po/

Testing Laser Cut Engrave Test File, Laser Cut Test File, Laser Cut File, Engrave File
https://www.etsy.com/listing/1068111114/laser-cut-engrave-test-file-laser-cut

Testing Lightburn Speed & Power Grid Tutorial
https://youtu.be/9-NlhJAS6t4

xTool

MakeBlock launches all-in-one xTool M1 desktop-cutting machine for DIYcreators
https://venturebeat.com/2021/10/26/makeblock-launches-all-in-one-xtool-m1.desktop-cutting-machine-for-diy-creators/

xTool M1 desktop CNC laser and blade cutting machine
https://www.geeky-gadgets.com/xtool-m1-desktop-cnc-laser-cutter-27-10-2021/

xTool D1 Laser Engraver LightBurn Set Up & First Project
https://www.youtube.com/watch?v=QZwpb_BZPI0

Part 1 of Testing out the xTool M1 - Unboxing the World's First Hybrid Laser & Blade Cutting Machine
https://www.youtube.com/watch?v=HBJS-kbjO8o

The Nicest Laser Engraver This Year? The xTool D1 Review
https://www.youtube.com/watch?v=85pafRzaf0s

xTOOL D1 Cut and Engrave FASTER, CLEAN and DETAIL
https://www.youtube.com/watch?v=VkHTjrx27ZE

Engrave and Cut Job Categories

Identification, Decoration, Labeling

Awards
Business card cases
Cell phone cases
Dog collars
Flasks
Key fobs
Keychains
Kitchen utensils
Knife handles
Kraft paper bags
Kraft paper labels
Notebooks
Pencils
Pens
Plaques
Tablet cases
Tool handles
Trophies

Jewelry

Bracelets
Broaches
Earrings
Necklaces
Pins
Watch bands
Wrist bands

Miniatures

Doll house furniture
Dioramas
HO train layouts & scenery
Museum displays
Scale models

Cylindrical Objects

Baseball bats
Drinking glasses
Mailing tubes
Mugs
Napkin holders
Ornaments
Pencil holders
Pencils
Pens
Rings

Rolling pins
Salt/Pepper shakers
Spice jars
Terra cotta pots
Water bottles
Wine bottle cork
Wine bottles
Wooden rolling pins

Spherical Objects

Ball bearings
Baseballs
Christmas ornaments
Glass spheres
Marbles
Soft balls
Tennis balls

General

3D Contour maps
Acrylic badges
Acrylic edge-lit lamps
Awards
Baby blocks
Back scratchers
Bird feeders
Bird houses
Book covers
Bookmarks
Business cards
Business signs
Cake toppers
Calendars
Can Openers
Candle stick holders
Canvas bags
Cell phone cases
Cell phone stands
Certificates
Cheese boards
Cheese plates
Chess/checker boards
Child's name puzzles
Christmas tree ornaments
Clocks
Clothes hangers
Clothing

Coaster holders
Coasters
Coffee pod holders
Coin banks
Cookbook stands
Cork-covered notebooks
Crowns and tiaras
Cut-out silhouettes
Cutting boards
Dart boards
Desk organizers
Desk storage boxes
Dice
Display racks
Door tags
Etched glass trays
Eyeglass cases
Fabric
Family trees
Food items
Game boards
Game pieces
Garden stakes
Garden stones
Gift boxes
Gift tags
Guest seating tags
Holiday Ornaments
House numbers
ID bracelets
Inspirational signage
Jewelry boxes
Jewelry stands
Jigsaw puzzles
Key holders
Lanterns
Leaf cut-outs
Leather patches & tags
Lighted acrylic picture frames
Living hinge boxes
Magnets
Marquetry & inlay boxes
Masks
Mirror engravings
Mirror frames
Mobiles
Mouse pads
Music boxes
Mustache combs
Name plates

Name tags
Napkin holders
Pad holders
Paper artwork
Paper cut-outs
Pencil/pen holder
Peppermills
Personalized stones
Pet memorials
Photo storage boxes
Picture frames
Place cards
Placemats
Plant holders
Plate display holders
Playing card holders
Puzzles
Reading glasses holders
Recipe boxes
Religious insignias
Rubber stamps
Rulers
Save-the-date bookmarks
Serving trays
Shadow boxes
Small toys
Street signs
Table lamps
Table numbers
Tablet stands
Tic-Tac-Toe games
Tissue boxes
Tool handles
Toothbrushes
Treat boxes
TV remote caddiesß
Wall hangings
Watch bands
Wax seal matrix
Wedding invitations
Wedding novelties
Welcome mats
Wind chimes
Wine boxes
Wood relief sculptures
Wood wall art
Wooden airplanes
Wooden signage
Wooden spoons

Resources for Prep and Finishing Laser-Processed Materials

Measuring: Determining physical properties

    Digital Vernier Caliper Measuring Tool. https://amzn.to/3l8lKd2

Cutting: Bringing workpieces down to size

    Breman Precision Self-Healing Cutting Mat 24x36 Inches. https://amzn.to/3ywLHuO

    Shinwa 24" Extruded Aluminum Cutting Rule Ruler Gauge. https://amzn.to/3Me6Dus

    Ludwig Precision Heavy-Duty Aluminum T-Square. https://amzn.to/37PZba8

    WorkPro Folding Utility Knife. https://amzn.to/38wKCs9

    Swingline Paper Cutter, Guillotine Trimmer. https://amzn.to/3lgVvkx

    Red Devil 1170 Plexiglass cutting tool. https://amzn.to/39riY04

    Hobby Knife Precision Knife Set. https://amzn.to/3L8sgeo

    Marshalltown17" Tile Cutter. https://amzn.to/3wsMl9Z

    Rockwell RK7323 BladeRunner X2 Portable Tabletop Saw. https://amzn.to/3Lm63tC

    Pack Weeding Craft Tool. https://amzn.to/3yHYUkF

Drilling: Producing precision holes

    Dremel Lite 7760 N/10 4V Li-Ion Cordless Rotary Tool. https://amzn.to/3NwnclR

    Milescraft 1097 ToolStand - Drill Press Stand. https://amzn.to/3MmWhc0

Sanding: Removing surface imperfections

    DEWALT Random Orbit Sander. https://amzn.to/3Pk3486

    Proxxon 28594 Pen Sander. https://amzn.to/37JrYgk

    BLACK+DECKER dustbuster Handheld Vacuum. https://amzn.to/3N9fDkC

    WEN 6502T Belt and Disc Sander https://amzn.to/3wZo6BU

Painting: Adding surface treatments

    Master Airbrush Cool Runner II Airbrushing System Kit. https://amzn.to/3FIbfXr

    Titanium Dioxide TiO2. https://amzn.to/3wbHFq8

    TUFFIOM Airbrush Spray Booth. https://amzn.to/3NgcZK8

Safety: Eye protection

    Ortur enclosure. https://amzn.to/3Pjo1zT

    FreeMascot Professional Laser Safety Glasses. https://amzn.to/3waO9Wf

Fire Suppression: Extinguishing flames

    Amerex B402, Fire Extinguisher. https://amzn.to/3wryYa6

Journaling: Recordkeeping

    Laser Engraving & Decorating Job Processing Record Book. https://amzn.to/3L8DRtW

FaceBook Groups

Acrylic Obsessed- Laser Edition
All Things Laser Engraving
Buy & Sell Laser Engraving Files/Crafts
CNC & Laser Vector file Sharing
CNC Acrylic Signs
CNC Designs
CNC Laser & Free Vector Files & Tech Support
CNC Tips, Tricks and Project Finishing
Custom Laser Engraving Blanks & Tutorials
Den of Lasers
Diode Laser Engraving
engraving on mirrors, glass, and tile
Everything Laser
Free Laser Engraving Files
Glass Etching & Laser Engraving
KW Custom Creations -Laser Supplies And Blanks
Laser - Jewelry Makers
Laser Cutting And Engraving
Laser Designer's Group
Laser Designs By Missa
Laser engrave & Cutting, File and Idea sharing
Laser Engraving
Laser Engraving & Cutting Files
Laser Engraving And Cutting
Laser Engraving and Cutting
Laser Engraving and Cutting for Grown ups
Laser Engraving Blanks

Laser Engraving Discussion Group
Laser Files
Laser life for dummies
Laser Livestream - Laser community
Laser Marking And Laser Engraving
Laser Parts,Materials,Supplies
Laser Rotary Group
Laser Wood Supplies
LASER WORLD
LaserWorld- Laser Cutting and Engraving
LightBurn Show & Tell
Lightburn Users supporting Lightburn Users
Louisiana Hobby Guy
Makeblock xTool Official Group
New to Laser Engraving
Official Ortur User Group
Ortur Advanced Users Group – Laser, 3D Printer, CNX
Ortur Laser Master (2) (PRO) 7W/15W/20W
Ortur Laser master 2 Pro User Group
Ortur Uncensored
Photo Laser Engraving
Tried and Tested Engraving, Sublimation and Printing Blanks and Materials
XTool D1 Classified Ads
xTool D1 Official Group
xTool D1 Owner Group
xTool D1 Unofficial Group
xTool M1 Official Group
xTool M1 Owner Group

Material Suppliers

Laserable Wood Plus

Colorado Heirloom Inc.
www.coloradoheirloom.com

Etsy
https://www.etsy.com/

Infinity Woods
www.infinitywoods.com

Lee's Wood Products
www.leeswoodproducts.com

MakerStock
https://makerstock.com

The Wood Gallery
https://thewoodgallery.com/

Totally Bamboo
www.totallybamboo.com

Trotec
https://www.engraving-supplies.com

WDI Company
www.wdicustomwood.com

Engravable Metal Plus

Alumamark
www.alumamark.com

Id Plates
www.idplates.com

Inland Products
www.inlandproducts.com

Inventables
www.inventables.com

Jelinek Cork Group
www.corkstore.com

NapTags
www.naptags.com

R. S. Owens
www.rsowens.com

Victory
www.buyvictory.com

Engravable Plastics Plus

Craft Closet
https://craftcloset.com/

Delvie's Plastics
https://www.delviesplastics.com/

Enduramark
https://www.enduramark.com

Gravotech
https://www.gravostoreusa.com

Innograv
https://www.innograv.com

Johnson Plastics Plus
https://www.jpplus.com

RoboSource
https://www.robosource.net

Smokey Hill Designs
https://smokeyhilldesigns.com

Metal Marking Compounds

Brilliance Laser Inks
https://brilliancelaserinks.com

CerMark Sales
https://cermarksales.com

Enduramark
https://enduramark.com

Laser Bonding Technology
www.laserbondingtech.com

markSolid
https://www.trotec-materials.com/news/laser-marking-products

Specialty Items

GS2 Awards & Laser Supply
www.gs2awards.com
plaques and trophies

I•Mark
www.imark-pen.com
pen and pencil sets

JDS Industries
www.jdsindustries.com
plaques and trophies

Free Vector Art

101 Free Downloads
https://www.1001freedownloads.com/free-vectors/

123FreeVectors
https://www.123freevectors.com/free-vector-download/free-vector-art/

All-Free Download
https://all-free-download.com/free-vector/totally-free-vector-images.html

Brands of the World
https://www.brandsoftheworld.com/

Creative Fabrica
https://www.creativefabrica.com/freebies/

Download Vector Print & Scan
https://www.ameede.com/category/scenery/

Dreamstime
https://www.dreamstime.com/

DXF for CNC Free Files
www.dxfforcnc.com

FlatIcon
https://www.flaticon.com/

Free Design File
https://freedesignfile.com/category/free-vector/

Free Graphics and Vectors
https://www.vecteezy.com/free-vector/dog

Free Laser Cut Files
www.thingiverse.com/tag:lasercut

Free Patterns Area
https://www.freepatternsarea.com/free-patterns-templates/

Free Vector
https://www.freevector.com

Free Vector Images
http://ww12.vectorgraphicart.com

Free Vector Maps
https://freevectormaps.com/

Free Vectors for Laser Cutting
www.3axis.co

Free Vectors
https://all-free-download.com/free-vector/vector-graphic.html

Freepik
https://www.freepik.com/vectors/graphics

Icon Monstr
https://iconmonstr.com/

Laser Cutting Material Template
https://www.thingiverse.com/thing:728579

Layered Paper Art - Laser Cut
https://www.layeredpaperart.com/free-files?fbclid=IwAR3zF_X7Zq0B3PyHsEhcolCBODbhq48M5i-Vdj-3WIYSZanHdpmV4fK7tipw

Ocon8
https://icons8.com/

Open Clipart
https://openclipart.org/

Ortur Thingiverse File
https://www.thingiverse.com/search?q=ortur&type=things&sort=relevant

Pimp My Drawing
https://pimpmydrawing.com/

Pixabay
https://pixabay.com/vectors/search/

Pixeden
https://www.pixeden.com/vectors

Public Domain Vectors
https://publicdomainvectors.org/

ShutterStock
https://www.shutterstock.com/vectors#free-download

Stockio
https://www.stockio.com/free-vectors/

Streamline
https://app.streamlinehq.com/icons

Texturelabs.org
https://texturelabs.org/

The Noun Project
https://thenounproject.com/

Vectarian
https://www.vectorian.net/

Vector 4 Free
https://www.vector4free.com/

Vector Art and Icons
https://www.vecteezy.com/free-vector/dog

Vector Files of Products
https://www.ameede.com/category/products/

Vector Portal
https://vectorportal.com/

Vector Stock
https://www.vectorstock.com/

Vectorish
http://vectorish.com/

Vectorization
https://www.vectorization.org/?fbclid=IwAR3N13Fn-VaEcQvWsZYmw-1PPs0aZwpHXkaWpfLLDdodZx_eKmfY7ZESWBeY

Vectorme
https://vector.me/

VectorStock
https://www.vectorstock.com/free-vectors

Vexels
https://www.vexels.com/free-vectors/

Wow Patterns
https://www.wowpatterns.com/pattern-generator

Free & Low-cost Fonts

1001 Free Fonts
https://www.1001freefonts.com/

Abstract Fonts
https://www.abstractfonts.com/

Adobe Fonts (For Creative Cloud subscribers)
https://fonts.adobe.com/?ref=tk.com

Artill
http://fonts.artill.de/collection/sketch_gothic

Awwwards
https://www.awwwards.com/awwwards/collections/free-fonts/

Befonts
https://befonts.com/

Behance https://www.behance.net/search/projects/?sort=appreciations&time=week&search=free%20font

Creative Fabrica
https://www.creativefabrica.com/freebies/free-fonts/

Dafont
https://www.dafont.com/

Deviant Art
https://www.deviantart.com/search?q=font

Dribble
https://dribbble.com/tags/free_font

Fawnt
http://www.fawnt.com/

Ffonts
https://www.ffonts.net/

Font Bundles
https://fontbundles.net/free-fonts

Font Diner
https://fontdiner.com/shop/free-fonts/

Font Freak
https://www.fontfreak.com/

Font M
https://fontm.com/

Font Planet
https://fontplanet.com/

Font Shop
https://www.fontshop.com/free-fonts

Font Shop
https://www.fontshop.com/free-fonts

Font Squirrel
https://www.fontsquirrel.com/

Font Zone
https://fontzone.net

Fontasy
http://www.fontasy.de/index.php?lang=en

FontFabric
https://www.fontfabric.com/free-fonts/

Fonts Arena
https://fontsarena.com/

FontSpace
https://fontspace.com

FontSpring
https://www.fontspring.com/free

Fontsty
https://fontsly.com

Free Design Resources
https://freedesignresources.net/category/free-fonts/

Free Script Fonts
https://www.freescriptfonts.net/

FreeTypography
https://freetypography.com

Google Fonts
https://fonts.google.com

Graphic Design Freebies
https://designshack.net/articles/typography/best-places-to-find-free-fonts/

Lost Type
http://www.losttype.com/

MyFonts https://www.myfonts.com/search/free%20fonts?freeFont=%5B%22Free+fonts+only%22%5D

Open Foundry
https://open-foundry.com/

Pinspiry Fonts
https://pinspiry.com/category/free-resources/fonts/

Pixel Surplus
https://pixelsurplus.com/collections/free-fonts

SHX fonts for LightBurn
https://forum.lightburnsoftware.com/t/shx-font-collection/25298

SHX fonts
https://www.cadtutor.net/forum/topic/13701-762-shx-autocad-fonts/

SHX script fonts
https://www.free-fonts.com/script-shx

Simply The Bes
http://simplythebest.net/fonts/

So Fontsy
https://sofontsy.com/collections/free

The Hungry JPEG
https://thehungryjpeg.com/freebies/free-fonts?utm_source=pixlrblog&utm_medium=blogpost&utm_campaign=Top5FreeFontSites

The League of Movable Type
https://www.theleagueofmoveabletype.com/

The Velvetyne Type Foundry
https://velvetyne.fr/

TypeType
https://typetype.org/freefonts/

Unblast
https://unblast.com/fonts/

Urban Fonts
https://www.urbanfonts.com/

Uxfree https://www.uxfree.com/category/fonts/

Free and Low-cost Images

Adobe Stock
https://stock.adobe.com/free

Burst
https://burst.shopify.com/

Creative Commons
https://search.creativecommons.org/

FAVPNG
https://favpng.com

Foca Stock
https://focastock.com/

Foodiesfeed
https://www.foodiesfeed.com/

Freestocks
https://freestocks.org/

Gratisography
https://gratisography.com/

ISO Republic
https://isorepublic.com/

Jay Mantri
https://jaymantri.com/

Kaboompics
https://kaboompics.com/

Lifeofpix
https://www.lifeofpix.com/

Little Visuals
https://littlevisuals.co/

New Old Stock
https://nos.twnsnd.co/

Open Peeps
https://www.openpeeps.com/

Pexels
https://www.pexels.com

Picjumbo
https://picjumbo.com

Picography
https://picography.co/

Picspree
https://picspree.com/en

Pixabay
https://pixabay.com/

Reshot
https://www.reshot.com/

Skitterphoto
https://skitterphoto.com

StockSnap.io
https://stocksnap.io

StockVault
https://www.stockvault.com

Styled Stock
https://styledstock.co/

Unsplash
https://unsplash.com/

Free & Low-cost Project Files

3axis.co
https://3axis.co/free-vectors/free+laser+cutting+projects

Black Cats
https://www.blackcatssvg.com/collections/free-files?fb-clid=IwAR21sv3leeIWmchoTv4Z0VHpDlwoghJCDg-SuIqOdAkOnQcyAdh-GE64BzjM

Box Designer
https://boxdesigner.connectionlab.org

Boxes.py
https://www.festi.info/boxes.py/?language=en

CNC Cookbook
https://www.cnccookbook.com/free-dxf-files/

CNC File Sharing
https://cncfilesharing.com

CNC Designshop
https://www.cncdesignshop.com/promotions/free-dxf-file-downloads.html

CNC DXF Files
https://cncdxffiles.com/product/starter-collection/

Cut Rocket
https://cutrocket.com/list/all/

Design a Badge
https://www.blackinton.com/design-a-badge/show-badge-catalog.php?PHPSESSID=i5b2o4j4ggl-j593113fp2fn882Post Production

Design Bundles
https://designbundles.net/free-design-resources

dfx1
https://dxf1.com/index.php

DXF for CNC
https://www.dxfforcnc.com/collections/free-dxf-files

DXF Store
https://dxfstore.com/free-dxf-files.html

DXFdownloads.com
https://www.dxfdownloads.com/category/free/

Epilog Laser Sample Club
www.epiloglaser.com/resources/sample-club.htm

Free DXF Files
https://mydxf.blogspot.com

Free Laser Cut Files
https://www.ponoko.com/free-laser-cutting-files-templates

Free Laser Files
http://www.freelaserfiles.com/files.html

Free Patterns Area
https://www.freepatternsarea.com

Free Patterns Area
https://www.freepatternsarea.com/free-projects/

FreeDXF
https://freedxf.com/product-category/free/

https://www.thingiverse.com/tag:lasercut

https://www.thingiverse.com/tag:lasercutter

Free SVG Cut Files
https://lovesvg.com/product-category/free-svg-files/

Gear Designer
http://www.jeromeleary.com/gears/

Gravini CUBE Designer
https://www.gravini.cz/en/laser-cube-online

Inventables
https://www.inventables.com/projects

Jigsaw Puzzle Generator
https://cncbloke.com.au/jigsaw.html?%20fbclid=IwAR-1GeNcsLOzbRqSm2nT2VxYFOVgPJggZ7A4OLHr-q56ttzzkvlGItf-%20ZhP7g

Laser Cutter Box
http://jeromeleary.com/laser/

Laser Ready Templates
https://laser-templates.com/collections/free-templates

Library Laser
https://www.librarylaser.com/en/free-laser-cut-files-3

LoveSVG
https://lovesvg.com/product-category/free-svg-files/

MakeCNC
https://www.makecnc.com

MakerCase
https://www.makercase.com/#/

Maker Design Lab
https://makerdesignlab.com/tag/free-laser-cutter-files/

Maker Union
https://www.makerunion.com/downloads/dxf/

MakerBot Thingiverse
https://www.thingiverse.com/search?q=laser+cut&-type=things&sort=relevant

Maslow Community Garden
http://maslowcommunitygarden.org/index.html

Multi Layer Mandala laser cut files
https://www.etsy.com/listing/816005365/photo-camera-multi-layer-mandala-model?ref=hp_rv-1&pro=1

Obrary
https://obrary.com/collections/open-designs

Scan2CAD
https://www.scan2cad.com/free-downloads/dxf/

Scrollsaw Workshop Pattern Catalog
https://www.stevedgood.com/catalog/index.php

SignTorch
https://www.signtorch.com/store/Free-Vector-DXF-Art-Samples

So Fontsy
https://sofontsy.com/collections/free

Thingiverse
https://www.thingiverse.com/tag:laser_cut

Trotek Template Downloads
https://www.troteclaser.com/en-au/knowledge/do-it-yourself-samples

Vecteezy
https://www.vecteezy.com/free-vector/laser-cut

Vision Engraving
https://www.visionengravers.com/support/vision-graphics-download.html

Wikiblock Library
https://www.betterblock.org/library

Index

Printed in Great Britain
by Amazon

47200151R10079